Young Readers Library

THE EARTH

by Arthur Beiser
and the Editors of TIME-LIFE BOOKS

TIME-LIFE INTERNATIONAL (Nederland) N.V.

ON THE COVER: A volcano in action, Mexico's Paricutín sends coloured arcs of flaming rock thousands of feet into the air. The volcano may spew over 2,000 tons of solid material in a single minute.

Contents

Preface

Serious study of the earth began with industry's search for raw materials—coal, oil, metals, building materials and water supplies. From this practical and fairly recent beginning, the earth sciences have matured, providing a far broader understanding of nature and of man's place in it.

The superb photographs and text of this book make it a fine introduction to the study of the earth and its processes. The story of the earth is both difficult and easy to read. No one can grasp it fully, yet everyone can find rewards in observing the scraps of records that lie everywhere about us. Every rock that crops out along a roadside, every feature of the natural landscape offers clues to its origin. A glacial boulder, an exposure of fossil-bearing limestone, the valley of a river—all will yield a wealth of information about their history.

The earth sciences are astir. Geophysics, geochemistry, biochemistry and other disciplines are being brought to bear on old questions about the history of rocks and landscapes, the origin of life, the causes of mountains, continents and oceans, and the earth's place in the universe. Surprising new facts and relationships are being discovered all the time. Some of the old problems are beginning to yield—at least a little. Man, with his passion for meaning and order, illuminates the record, and the story of the earth grows more fascinating every year.

WILLIAM W. RUBEY
Professor Emeritus of Geology and Geophysics
University of California, Los Angeles

1

A Small but Very Special Planet

THE BLUE PACIFIC, dotted with clouds that seem to float on its surface, stretches to the edge of the world in this picture taken by an astronaut soaring at an altitude of 100 miles. Beyond, the deep blackness of space outlines the curve of the earth, which is clearly noticeable at this height.

This is a journey to the earth. The trip begins far out in the universe, within a cluster of galaxies that are huddled together in what astronomers call a "local group". One member of this cosmic family, itself made up of countless stars, has a graceful pinwheel-like form. This is the Milky Way. As galaxies go it is only of medium size, yet its dimensions are hard for the mind to grasp. From one edge to the other it measures some 100,000 light-years. Its central bulge is as much as 25,000 light-years thick. And one light-year—the distance that light travels in a year at the speed of 186,234 miles a second—is just under six million million miles.

Two-thirds of the way from the centre of the Milky Way, where the stars begin to thin out, there shines an ordinary, yellowish star. It has plenty of room in which to move around, for its nearest neighbour in the galaxy is 4 light years—24 million million miles—away. This lonely star, which glows from afar as weakly as a fire-fly, is our sun. Among its own family of faithfully circling planets, satellites, asteroids, meteoroids and comets, one oddly matched

Strange Ideas about the World

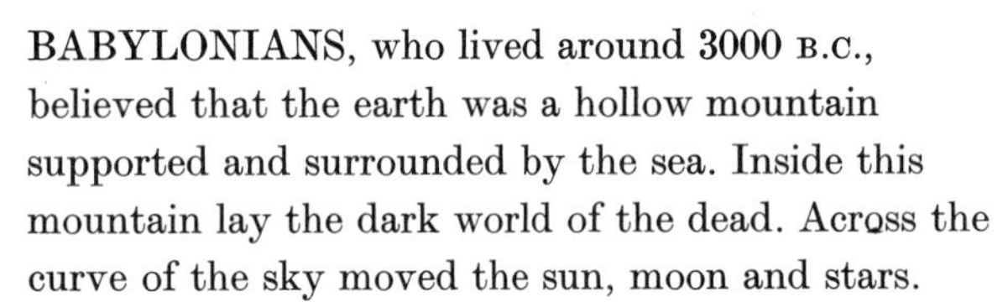

BABYLONIANS, who lived around 3000 B.C., believed that the earth was a hollow mountain supported and surrounded by the sea. Inside this mountain lay the dark world of the dead. Across the curve of the sky moved the sun, moon and stars.

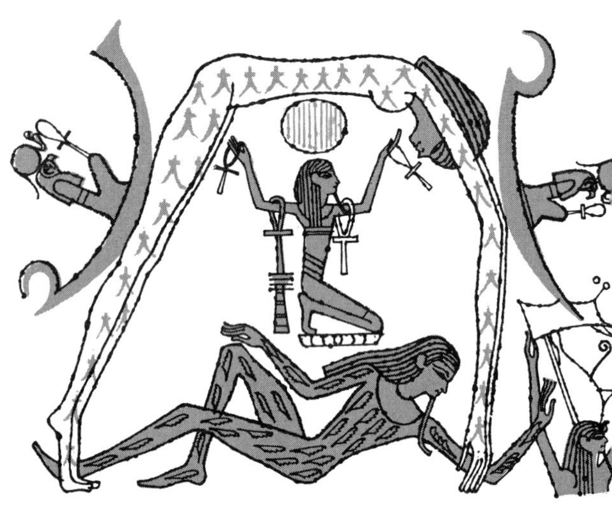

EGYPTIANS saw the earth as a resting god and the heavens as a gracefully bent goddess. Between them sat the god of the atmosphere, supporting the skies, The sun god, shown in his boat, sailed each day across the heavens into the death of night.

pair is the earth and its companion, the moon.

A minor planet bound to an ordinary star in the outskirts of one galaxy among millions of millions—this is the earth. Approached in this way, from the chill reaches of infinite space, it would be all too easy to miss—a speck almost beneath notice except for one thing: of all the places that might possibly support human life, the earth is the only place we know of that does. Its interior and its "skin", its atmosphere, its climate and even its behaviour in space, form an environment in which life flourishes.

Long before men had any real understanding of the shape or size of their planet, of its humble place in the universe, they felt in their bones that each native valley, sheltered harbour or game-rich plain they lived in was somehow central to the entire cosmic scheme of things. In ancient Greece, all the gods of the universe were thought to dwell on a medium-sized mountain, Olympus, 150 miles from Athens. China, although torn and occupied again and again by barbarians, has always held firmly to the proud little title of "Central Nation". Behind each of these and many similar sentiments lay a certain logic; after all, any man is

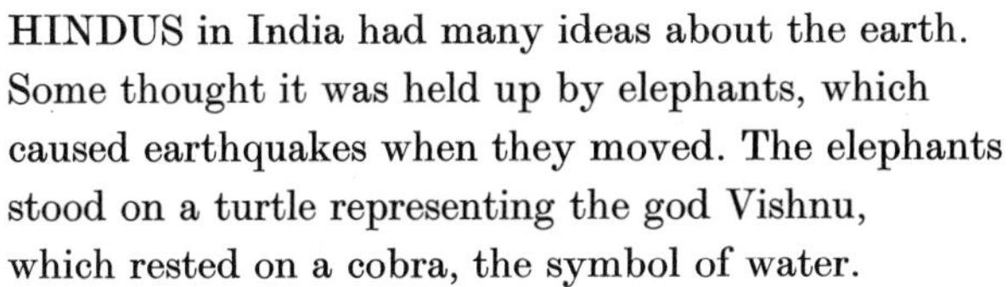

HINDUS in India had many ideas about the earth. Some thought it was held up by elephants, which caused earthquakes when they moved. The elephants stood on a turtle representing the god Vishnu, which rested on a cobra, the symbol of water.

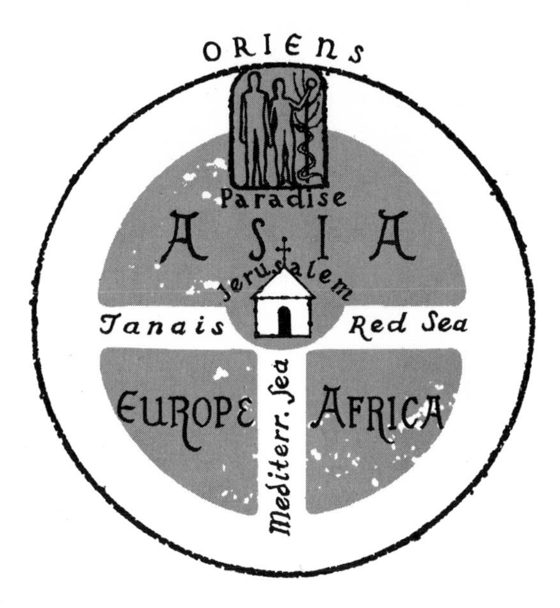

CHRISTIANS of the Middle Ages based their ideas on religious views. They divided the earth into three continents, with Jerusalem at the centre and the Garden of Eden in Asia. The word Tanais stands for the river Don, an important trade route then.

the centre of his own circular horizon; any kingdom is the centre of surrounding kingdoms; to man the earth is the centre of the universe. It was a long time before anyone really thought about the size of the planet itself.

Though earlier philosophers had concluded that the earth was a globe, it was not until about 250 B.C. that an Alexandrian Greek, Eratosthenes, used geometry on the problem of the earth's total dimension. In Syene, an Egyptian town some 5,000 stadia (500 miles) south of Alexandria, there was a deep, dry well. Eratosthenes learned that at noon on the longest day of the year the sun's light shone directly down the well shaft. In Alexandria on that same day, he knew, the noon sun was not vertical, but cast a slight shadow. Eratosthenes used a simple geometric calculation to show that the difference in angle between Syene and Alexandria was about one-fiftieth of a circle. So, 5,000 stadia multiplied by 50 gave Eratosthenes the first close estimate of the earth's circumference that we know about. Translating from stadia to miles, his amazingly accurate measurement comes out to 25,000 miles for the circumference (the modern figure at the equator is 24,902) and 8,000

miles for the diameter of the earth (the modern mean is 7,917 miles).

For such rough measurement, Eratosthenes' achievement was remarkable, but was somehow ignored or lost. So it was that Christopher Columbus, 1,700 years later, set off westwards around the world to reach the Indies with a far smaller earth in mind. Despite what folklore says, Columbus knew—as did any other master mariner of his day—that the earth was a sphere; what he did not know was the earth's true size.

Today, thanks especially to measurements that were made during the International Geophysical Year (1957-1958), we know exactly what the earth's dimensions are. Indeed, the IGY men were aware long before that the earth was not a perfect sphere. Even before this fact was demonstrated by measurement, Isaac Newton had predicted it. Field work in the 18th century confirmed Newton's prediction—

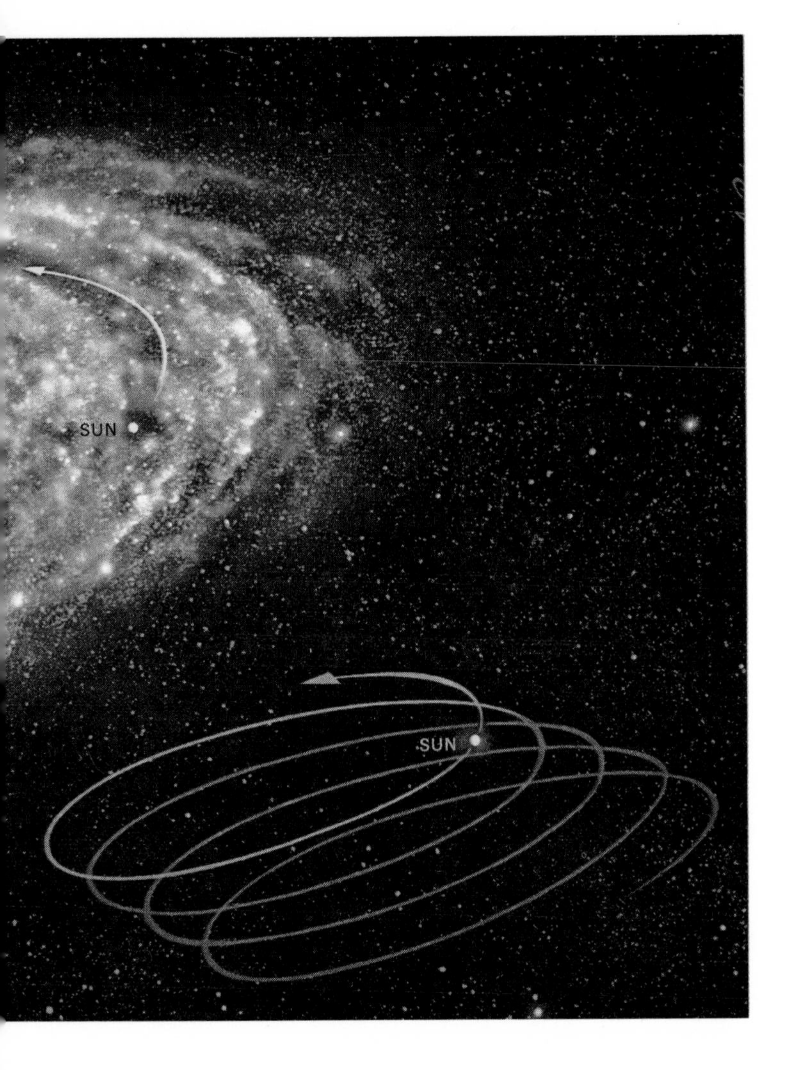

Spiralling into Space

As the earth and the other planets orbit round the sun, the sun itself moves through space at 150 miles per second (*small arrow, left*), swinging round with the other stars of the Milky Way in its own kind of orbit once every 200 million years. At the same time the whole Milky Way is plunging along through space (*large arrow*). The two motions together make the sun and its family of planets trace a spiral path (*lower right*).

that at the equator the earth is 26.7 miles thicker than it is when measured from Pole to Pole. Even more exact measurements, based on the movements of America's IGY Vanguard I satellite, have shown that the highest points of the equatorial bulge (a matter of 25 feet) lie a little to the south of the earth's equatorial mid-line.

For most purposes though, the earth might as well be round. If all our planet's dimensions were shrunk to a globe about five feet across, the human eye could not detect the difference—about a fifth of an inch—between the diameter at the equator and the Poles. A fine coat of paint would be thicker than the continents' average height above sea level, and a light pin-prick would probe this model earth's crust more deeply than have man's deepest oil wells.

Human beings may soon gain such a scaled-down view of their planet by travelling the nearer regions of space. From near-by

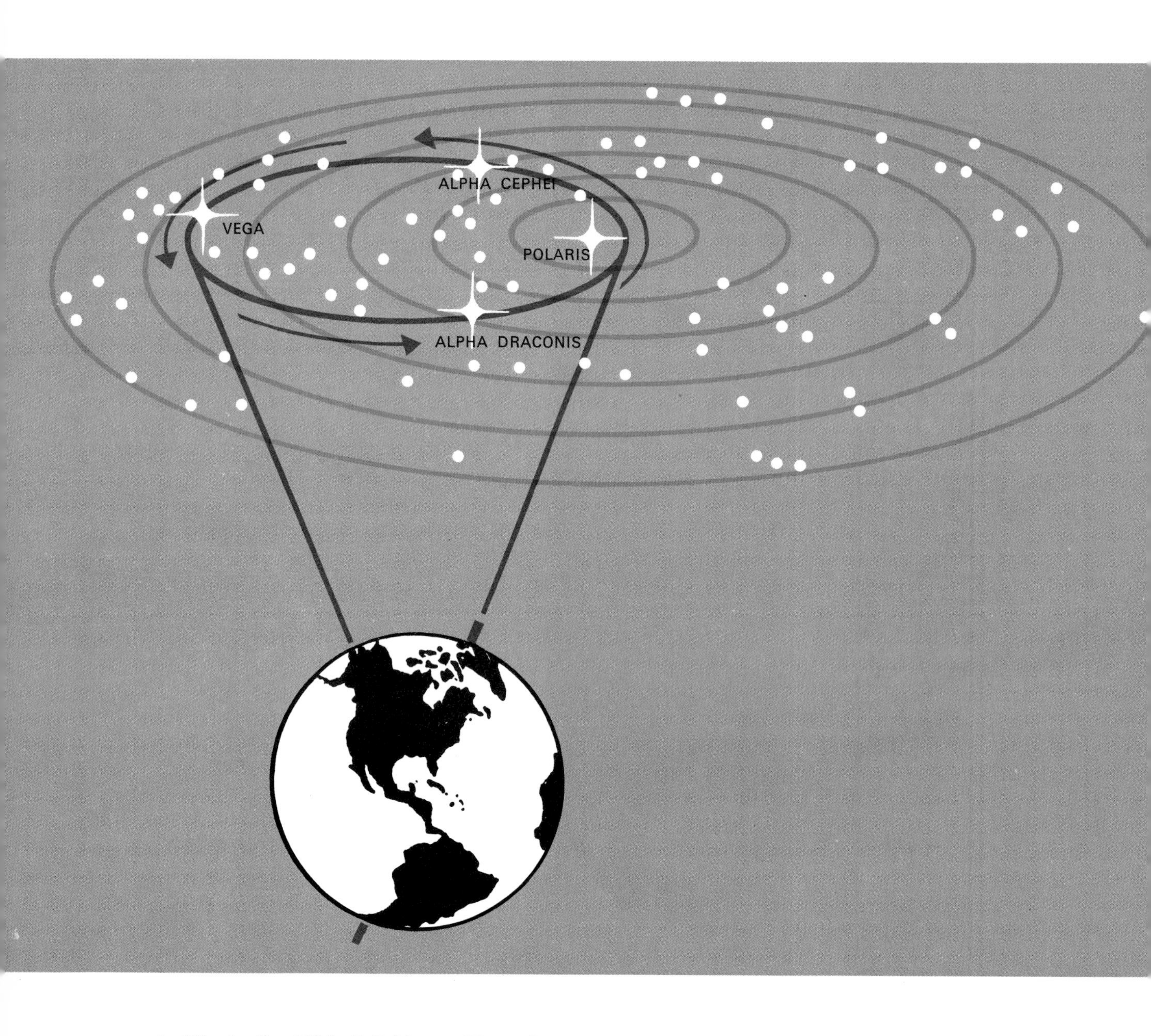

A Slowly Wobbling Earth

Over a period of 22,000 years, the axis of the earth shifts, describing a complete circle like the slowly weaving head of a spinning top. Today the axis points to Polaris, which we use as our "North Star". By the year A.D. 7500, it will point to Alpha Cephei; by A.D., 14,000, to Vega. Then it will swing around to Alpha Draconis—which was the North Star 5,000 years ago—before returning to point once again to Polaris.

space the earth would appear as a colourful, ever-changing globe. Its sunlit face would show a bluish appearance, while its companion in space, the moon, would have a yellow cast. Colour rather than geographic landmarks would distinguish the earth's continents from its oceans: the land areas would appear to be a delicate red-brown, the water light blue-green. A dazzling splash of light would mark the sun's reflection on any water surface.

Large events on the earth would be fairly easy to follow. The annual cycle of vegetation would be reflected in colour changes on the continents, and it might even be possible to trace the seasonal advance and retreat of the snow cover in the high latitudes of the Northern Hemisphere. Clouds would be conspicuous, often arrayed in long lines with clear gaps between them. From the drift of these white wisps across the surface, an observer could follow both the westward flow of the trade winds and the eastward procession of the major weather systems in the earth's middle latitudes.

Other phenomena would be harder to detect. A good telescope should pick out the night-time glow of great cities, however, and a sensitive radio receiver would reveal that at least a portion of man's multitude of radio signals penetrates the upper zones of the earth's atmosphere and passes on into space. From there an observer could watch the variety of motions in which the earth is engaged. The most obvious of these is the earth's daily rotation on its own axis. This is the motion that gives us day and night as each place on the earth faces towards or away from the sun. The earth also revolves around the sun in the period of time we call a year, a 600-million-mile sweep that takes almost exactly 365¼ days. This trip round the sun, combined with the earth's tilt, is the movement that is responsible for the seasons.

The earth's axis, the imaginary line between the North and South Poles, does not stand straight up and down in relation to the sun. If it did, the equator would always point directly towards the sun, and there would be no seasons, just perpetual summer at the equator and eternal winter at the poles.

But this is not the case. When it is winter in the Northern Hemisphere, the North Pole points away from the sun, and the South Pole points towards the sun. This is why the seasons north of the equator are the exact opposite of those in the south. The longest day of the north's year (and the beginning of the summer season) falls around the 21st of June, which is the shortest day of the south's year and the beginning of its winter.

Yet another movement causes the earth's axis to point to different parts of the sky. This movement is very slight, and terribly difficult to detect. But it has one noticeable effect: over a period of thousands of years the axis points at one, then another, then

Clear and Cold

Because the earth's axis is tilted in relation to its path around the sun, the Northern and Southern Hemispheres do not receive equal amounts of sunshine at any given time. When the Northern Hemisphere is tilted away from the sun, the sun's rays strike it on a slant, producing less warmth. This brings winter to a place like London (*black dot on the right*), with snow and frosty scenery (*below*). At the same time, it is summer in the Southern Hemisphere.

another star, and the star we call the North Star changes. The ancient Egyptians, living 5,000 years ago, had a different north star from the one we have today. Their star, named Alpha Draconis, was in the Draco constellation. Our north star, Polaris, is in the Little Dipper. About 12,000 years from now the north star will be Vega, the brightest star in the northern sky. Even further in the future, in the year A.D. 28,000, Polaris will again be the north star, and the cycle will repeat itself, as it has for hundreds of millions of years.

In addition to these movements, the earth shares two more motions with the other members of the solar system. In one of these, the earth follows the sun's own 12-mile-per-second journey through our local star cloud in the general direction of the constellation Hercules. In the other motion, the earth follows the sun in its major journey—a great, wheeling sweep around the hub of the Milky Way that takes 200 million years to complete.

From a point in near-by space we could also observe the unusual nature of the earth's neighbour, the moon. Satellites of the outer planets are as big as or bigger than our moon—Jupiter's Ganymede is

Warm and Wet

When the Northern Hemisphere tilts towards the sun, the sun's rays strike it more directly, producing higher temperatures. In addition, a given spot stays in the larger sunlit zone for a longer period of time as the earth rotates; on the day in late June that the axis tilts closest to the sun, London (*dot*) gets a full 15 hours of daylight. The higher temperatures and increased hours of sunlight produce the welcome scenery of green forests.

three times as large—but no other body in the sun's family has proportionally as large a companion as the earth does. The moon is not only very close to the earth but it has a diameter that is more than a quarter that of the earth's and more than two-thirds that of Mercury's. Scientists now think that the moon may have been formed as a planet, either taking shape as a near twin from the same raw material as the earth or forming elsewhere and later being captured by the earth.

We cannot study the earth's history as a planet without also studying the moon. This lesser twin circles the earth in an elliptical orbit once each $27^{1}/_{3}$ days. With each such revolution, the moon also rotates on its axis exactly once, so that the earth's inhabitants never see the "back" of the moon. Actually, the moon's axis is tilted, so that we glimpse both its north polar and south polar regions; in addition, its shape and motions are irregular enough for its swaying and nodding to have permitted us to photograph 59 per cent of the moon's total surface from the earth. Brilliantly lighted by the sun during the lunar day, the earthward face of the moon is dimly illuminated during the lunar night by sunlight reflected from the earth. An ideal

subject for photography, the moon's visible surface has been mapped in detail. Photographs of the far side, radioed back to earth during rocket space probes, show it to be quite like the near side.

The airless, waterless landscape of the moon is dramatically marked by vast dark plains (once thought by astronomers to be seas and hence named *maria*, a Latin word meaning "seas"). Its jagged peaks are as high as or higher than the largest of the earth's mountains. Its thousands of spectacular craters are as much as 180 miles across. Since the moon has no real atmosphere, and so no rain or running water, the sort of erosion that continually softens the landscape of the earth is unknown there. Its sharp-edged features are smoothed only by meteorites, and by the savage wrenches of expansion and contraction, as the scorching heat of day—90° C.—is followed by a night chill that may drop to about −180° C.

What does the lunar landscape tell us about the earth's own past? Once it was believed that the craters on the moon represented a long series of volcanic eruptions such as the earth has often known. Today most astronomers believe these surface scars are marks left by ancient meteorites. Following this clue in recent years, we have detected the nearly vanished traces of similar, stupendous collisions on the earth.

(Text continued on page 20)

"Earthshine" on the Moon

An artist's drawing of the moon's barren landscape shows a mamoth crater bathed in sunlight reflected from the earth, seen in the distance on the right. A few years ago such illustrations, based on earth-bound telescope sightings, were the only views of what the moon's surface might be like. Since then space vehicles have taken close-up photographs (*next page*).

Learning from the Moon

We may learn more about the history of our solar system from the moon than we can from the earth's surface, which is constantly changing. Most of the lunar surface today is very much as it was 2,000 million years ago. Meteorites continue to pock the moon with craters such as the mountain-studded Copernicus crater, shown above. This crater—which is as large as the island of Cyprus—appears by itself in the centre of the picture on the opposite page. Lunar topsoil, seen under one of Surveyor I's footpads on the right, may be made from meteorite rubble, or it may be powdery lava rock like that found on earth.

Human explorers on the moon will learn much about the nature of matter in space, and so about the history of our own planet. Meanwhile, other sorts of clues are available. These come from studies of the chunks, lumps, fragments and specks of dust that continually rain down upon the earth from outer space.

Not long ago many people believed that the brief flashes in the night sky that we now know are meteor trails were somehow involved with the atmosphere and with the weather in general ("meteor", from which we get our word "meteorology", comes from the Greek for "high in the air"). There was logic in such a view; but it was based on the inaccurate assumption that lightning bolts produced something called "thunderstones"—which were actually peculiar rocks, or more often, the crude, unrecognized flint tools of early man.

Meteor flashes, too, were sometimes accompanied by thunderous sounds and unidentifiable fragments of stone or iron. Even with today's understanding, the matter of meteors still involves complex language. Specialists are very careful to distinguish between *meteoroids* (the bits of matter, regardless of size or composition, that drift through space), *meteors* (the flashes of light produced by a meteoroid as it is heated glowing hot by its passage through the earth's atmosphere), and finally *meteorites* (the fragments, ranging from dust to huge rocks, that survive the fiery passage and

Our Meteorite Relatives

The composition of meteorites, like that of the moon, gives us clues to the make-up of the earth, because they too were formed from matter in our solar system. The pock-marked chunk on the right is an iron-nickel meteorite that landed in Oregon in the American North-West in 1902. It is the largest ever recovered in this country and weighs 12½ tons. The huge crater below, four-fifths of a mile across and 600 feet deep, was made in the south-western U.S. State of Arizona in prehistoric times by a 13,000-ton meteorite that exploded and scattered into dust.

reach the earth). Meteorites are the only samples of material from space that men can now study. As a result, meteorites are as fascinating to students of the earth as they are to astronomers.

Meteorites are of three general classes: irons—composed 98 per cent or more of nickel-iron; stony irons—composed roughly half-and-half of nickel-iron and a kind of rock known as olivine; and finally stones. All offer useful clues to the history of the earth, for not only are meteorites fellow members of the solar system, but they are probably as old as the earth itself.

A few spectacular falls have brought irons weighing as much as 30 tons smashing into the earth. But apart from these, a vast amount of meteoritic dust continually falls from the heavens, perhaps as much as several million tons every year. This dust consists of tiny particles ranging in size from one ten-thousandth to one hundredth of an inch across. Meteoritic dust particles have been found around the world and because many of them contain iron, they may be extracted magnetically from rain water.

Many meteor showers occur in streams with established orbits. Some of these orbits are known to be the same as the orbits of former comets. Therefore, one might suppose that meteor showers represent the debris left in the wake of comets, past or present. But it is doubtful whether such "comet dust" meteors are ever large enough, by the time they reach the earth's surface, to be studied. The particles are so small that by the time they are burned in the atmosphere there is almost nothing left.

Many scientists feel that the meteors that do reach the earth as meteorites are fragments of asteroids; a belt of these objects orbits the sun between Mars and Jupiter. It is likely that many meteorites were once asteroid fragments that were knocked from their paths into orbits that brought them within the field of the earth's gravitational pull. But whatever their source, the meteorites that have fallen and continue to fall to the earth—and which in the past pockmarked the moon—offer tantalizing clues to the composition of those interior parts of our planet that lie beyond reach, and clues to the earth's origin as well.

Through a Million Million Years

The mightiest gorge on any continent, the Grand Canyon in Arizona, U.S.A., reveals rock more than a million million years old where the river Colorado has cut 6,000 feet deep into arid plateau land. The river has been carving out the rocky valley for 10 million years, and will continue to do so for millions yet to come.

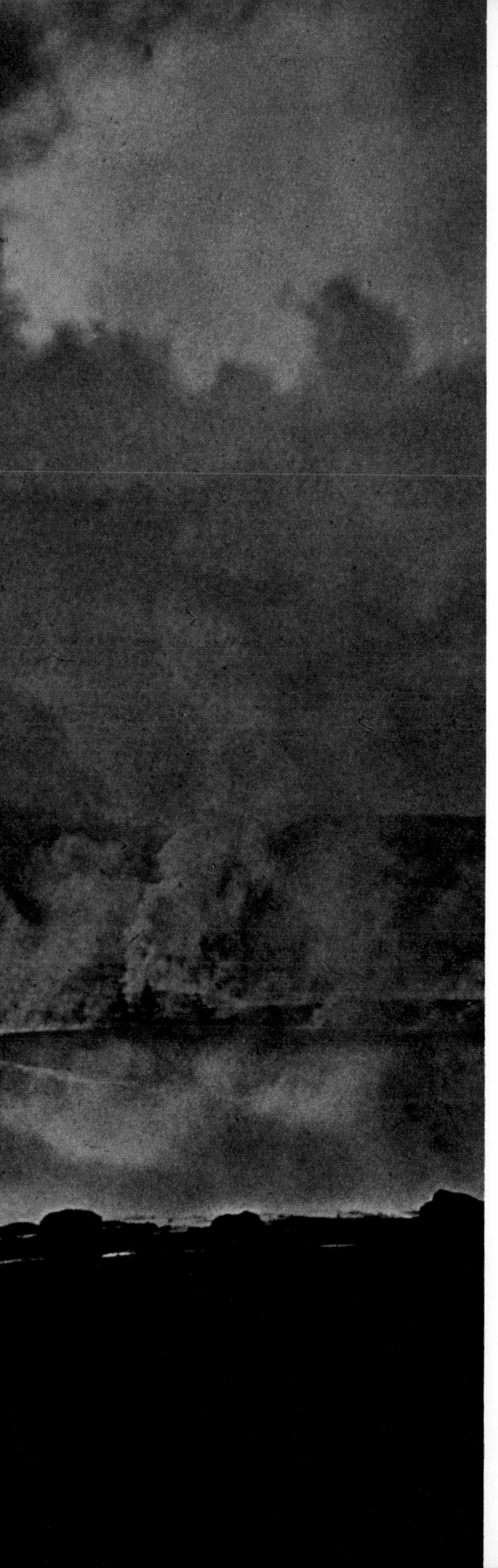

2

Cloudy Beginnings of the Earth

While man has long known about the earth's size and shape, his understanding of the planet's origin—and exactly what it is made of—is much less complete.

The earth has certainly not existed for ever. If it had, radioactive elements still in its crust would have decayed into different, inactive elements long ago. The earth is old indeed—today most geologists accept a figure of 4,500 million years—but once upon a time there was no earth, and how it was born presents one of the most fascinating riddles in science.

There has been no lack of attempted solutions. Some ancient mythologies pictured the young earth as a warm body of liquid. The philosopher Descartes in 1644 saw it as a sun-like, glowing body. Immanuel Kant and the Marquis de Laplace, in the 18th century, thought it had condensed out of a

THE BOIL AND BUBBLE of this unearthly scene is an imaginary view of what a young earth looked like millions of millions of years ago. At this point in its development, much of the surface rock was so hot that it was liquid. The heat also kept most of the water hanging in the sky as clouds of steam.

gaseous cloud surrounding the sun. Other hypotheses held that the earth was thrown out of a sun made unstable by its enormous rate of spin, or torn away from it by the force of a collision, or near-collision, with some passing star.

The whole question of the earth's evolution is, of course, linked to the larger questions of the origin of the solar system, of stars in general, of galaxies—and of the entire universe. Man tries to answer these questions with theories, but it is beyond his power to know exactly what happened.

With this warning, what can be said about the earth's first days? Many astronomers now agree that a chain of events probably started inside a huge cloud of gases and dust that measured farther across than the entire solar system does today. For a long time this dust cloud may have been formless, but at some point the force of gravity working within the cloud caused it to collapse into a flattened, revolving disc.

Today there are two theories that attempt to explain what happened within that huge dust cloud to form the sun and its planets. The first suggests that the dust and gases near the centre drew together to form the solar system's largest body, the sun. The planets were formed in a similar way: the remainder of the cloud was formed into rings or eddies; eventually the material in these contracted to form the planets.

The second theory holds that most of the material in the cloud went into the for-

The Fires Within Burst Out

Heat from inside the earth seeps out slowly through cracks in the surface, and now and then bursts out violently in the form of volcanoes and geysers. The steaming crater of Nyamlagira volcano in Africa (*left*) is a scene of broken rock and clouds of gas. The fiery fountains of Kilauea in Hawaii (*above*) spew forth a lava lake. It was lava from thousands of such eruptions under water that built up volcanoes until they emerged as the Hawaiian Islands.

mation of what was to become the sun. As this "protosun" grew it began spinning so fast that it cast off rings and these condensed to form the planets.

No matter which theory is eventually proved correct, the result is the same. At some point in the formation of the solar system the sun began to shine; the planets grew warm and their veils of gas evaporated. After hundreds of millions of years what remained was the sun-warmed, shrunken inner planets and the gas-enveloped outer planets, which have not changed since.

One bit of evidence that seems to support this theory is the orderliness of the solar system. For example, if the sun and all the planets were formed from the same spinning cloud of dust and gases, they would all tend to spin in the same direction. And they all do, except for Venus, which for some unknown reason has a reverse spin. However, all the planets—even Venus—travel in the same direction round the sun, and all are in a fairly flat plane around the sun's equator.

There is one exception: Pluto, the planet farthest from the sun, has a very irregular orbit. Some scientists think it may have once been a moon belonging to Neptune, its nearest neighbour, and escaped from its original orbit to become a planet in its own right. But until astronomers learn more about how the planets got their satellites, this is only an educated guess.

Until the earth could be weighed, no one could be sure what it was made of.

A Many-Layered Sphere

If we could slice open the earth, we might see five distinct layers of matter like those in the drawing on the right. Beneath a thin crust 3 to 40 miles thick are the two layers of the mantle composed of denser and denser rock. Below these, some scientists believe, is an iron core divided into two parts. The outer core is liquid but the inner core is probably solid, due to the massive pressure on it. This core is the hot spot of the planet—the temperature there is believed to be between 2,000°C. and 4,500°C.

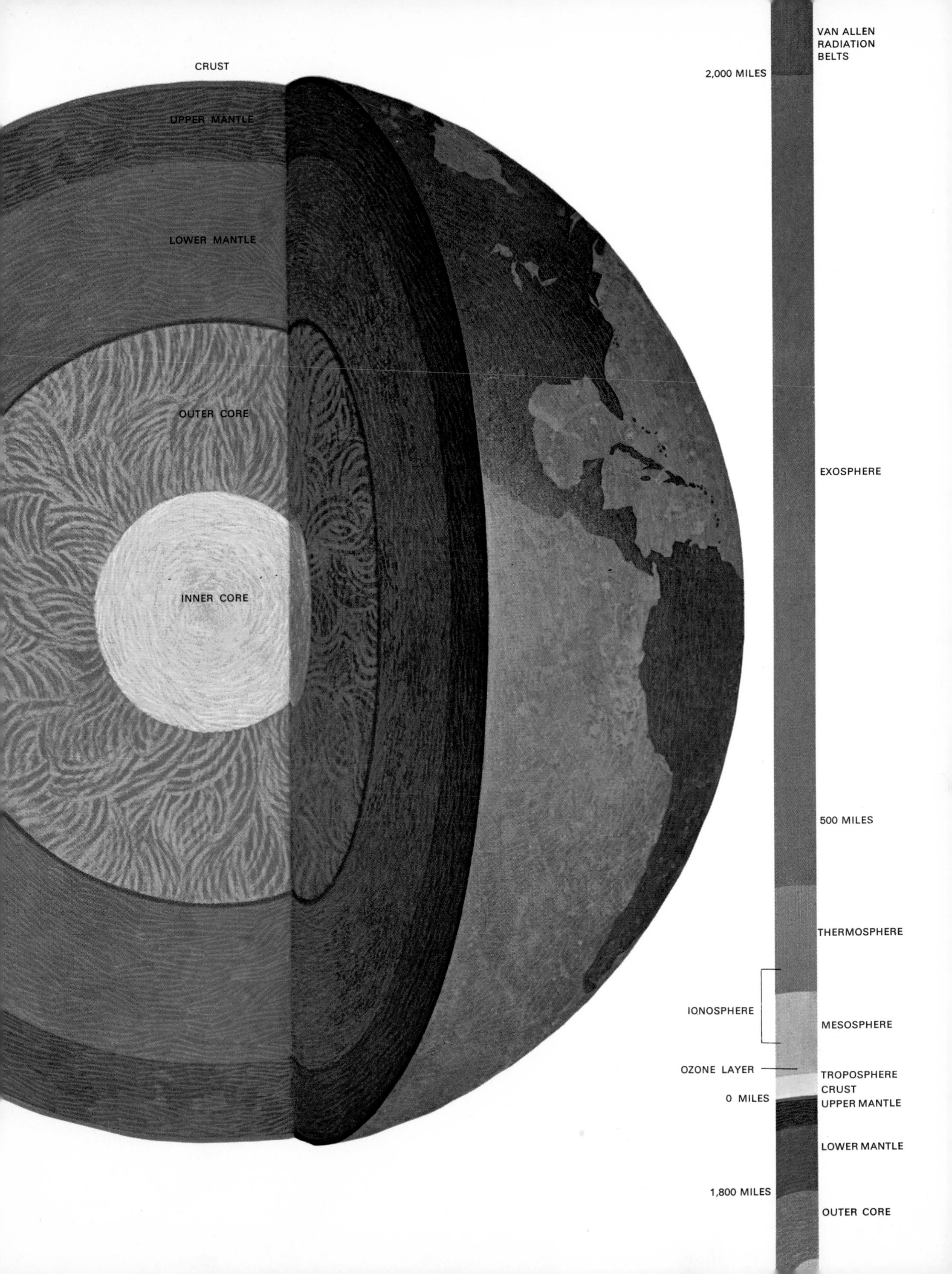

CRUST

UPPER MANTLE

LOWER MANTLE

OUTER CORE

INNER CORE

VAN ALLEN RADIATION BELTS

2,000 MILES

EXOSPHERE

500 MILES

THERMOSPHERE

IONOSPHERE

MESOSPHERE

OZONE LAYER

TROPOSPHERE

CRUST

0 MILES

UPPER MANTLE

LOWER MANTLE

1,800 MILES

OUTER CORE

Steam from the Underworld

When the earth's underground water strikes hot rock, it turns into superheated steam, which forces its way through holes in the surface called fumaroles. This action is part of the earth's water cycle, in which water passes from the earth into the air, then falls again as rain, running under the ground or in rivers to the sea.

But there were plenty of suggestions. One was that the earth was filled with water, and that it was this water, released by some terrible eruption, that caused the Biblical flood. Some people proposed that the earth's crust was dust, which floated on a bath of oil. Others believed the earth to be hollow, and perhaps filled with fire.

Finally, in 1798, the English physicist Henry Cavendish "weighed" the earth. Measuring the gravitational attraction between model spheres, and using a complex formula, he arrived at a weight of 5,900 million million million (5.9 followed by 21 zeros) tons. As estimates go, it was a good one.

For its volume, which is about 260,000 million cubic miles, the earth is the second densest planet in the solar system. Its average density is five and a half times that of water. (Saturn, at the other extreme, is so light that it could float in water—if there were an ocean large enough to hold it.) But the average density of the rocks that make up the earth's crust is too low to account for such a heavy planet. To the scientists who first thought about this, one fact was immediately clear: the density of the earth's interior had to be far greater than that of the surface rocks.

Even today, no one can be absolutely certain of what lies beneath the earth's crust. But scientists are learning, largely through studying earthquakes.

Although only about 20 severe earthquakes wrench the earth each year, there are approximately a million minor tremors during the same period, or about two a minute. They provide continuous information about the earth's interior. As a result of a century of study, seismologists (scientists who study earthquakes) know that nearly all the major earthquakes begin in two long, narrow zones. The principal zone is a belt in the lands that border the Pacific Ocean, running up the west coast of North and South America, and down the coast of Asia. The second major zone runs from west to east across Europe and Asia—from Spain, along northern Africa through Italy, Greece, Turkey, India and Burma—to join the Pacific belt. The first zone, known as the Pacific "ring of fire" because most of the world's volcanoes are along its path, is also the site of about 80 per cent of all earthquakes. The second zone is responsible for an additional 15 per cent or so. The remaining quakes occur at scattered places elsewhere on the earth.

Nearly all earthquakes are caused by the fracturing, or breaking, of the solid rock of the earth's crust along one or another of these zones. These fractures, called faults, occur when stresses that develop within the earth become too great for the brittle crust to bear. A spectacular example is the San Andreas fault in California. The land mass east of the San Andreas fault is steadily inching its way south, and every so often the motion goes beyond the stretching ability of the underlying rock. When this

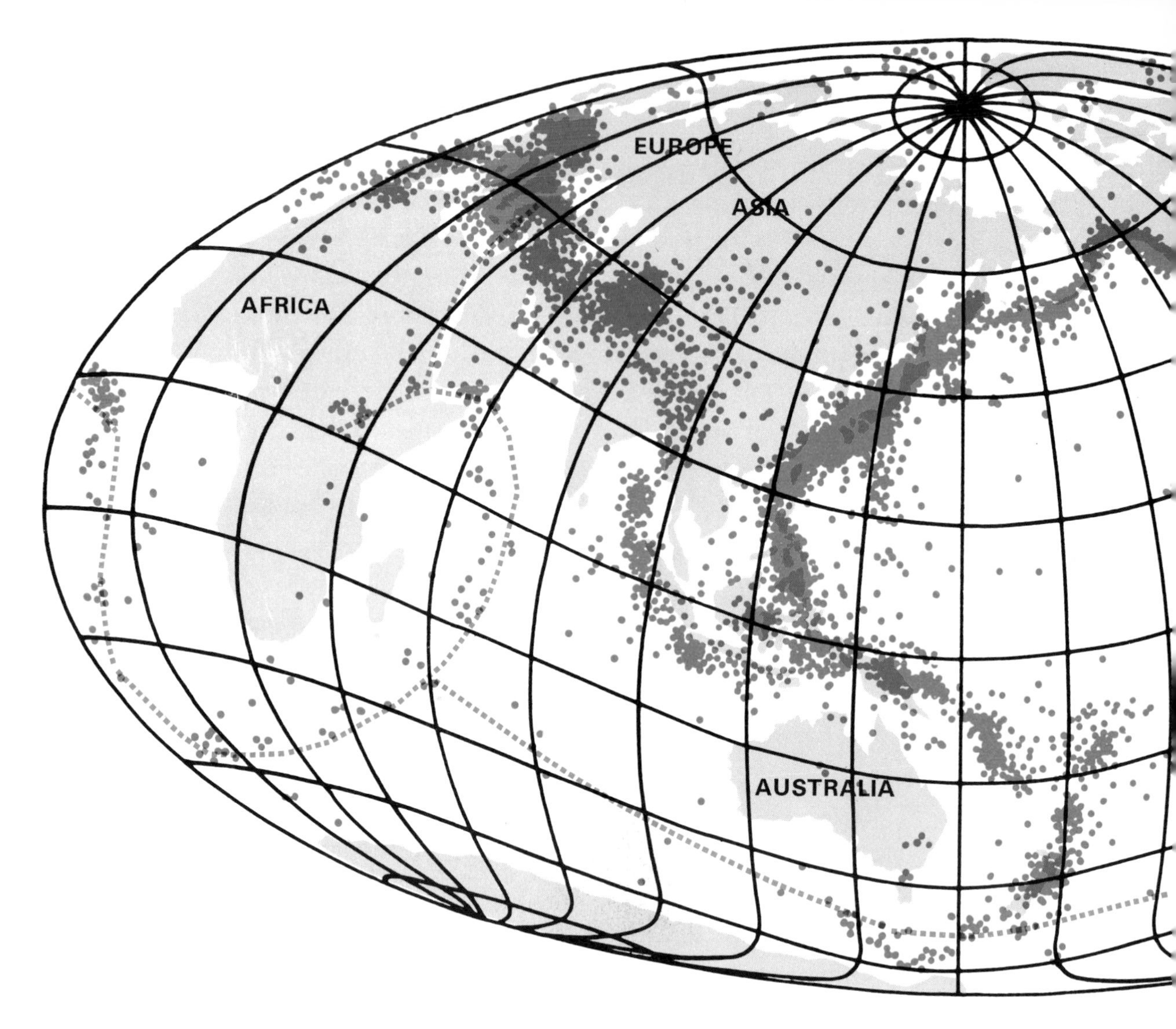

happens, the rock breaks. On the 18th of April 1906, the ground shifted as much as 15½ feet along 200-odd miles of the San Andreas fault, causing the earthquake that demolished much of San Francisco. It was one of the biggest earth shifts ever recorded for a single quake.

The 1906 San Francisco earthquake was neither the first nor the last to occur as the result of movement along the Pacific Coast faults: major earthquakes shook California in 1857, 1922 and 1940, and others can be expected to take place from time to time before the rearrangement of the earth's crust in that restless region is complete.

A major earthquake is one of nature's most awesome events. In violence it may exceed the detonation of a million million tons of TNT, and while the most severe disturbance is local, the shock may be felt over wide areas. The Lisbon earthquake of 1755, for example, not only wrecked the heart of the city and killed thousands of its people, but also made itself felt over a million and a half square miles of Europe. All over the Continent the waters of lakes and rivers were violently disturbed, and sea waves from the quake rushed all the way across

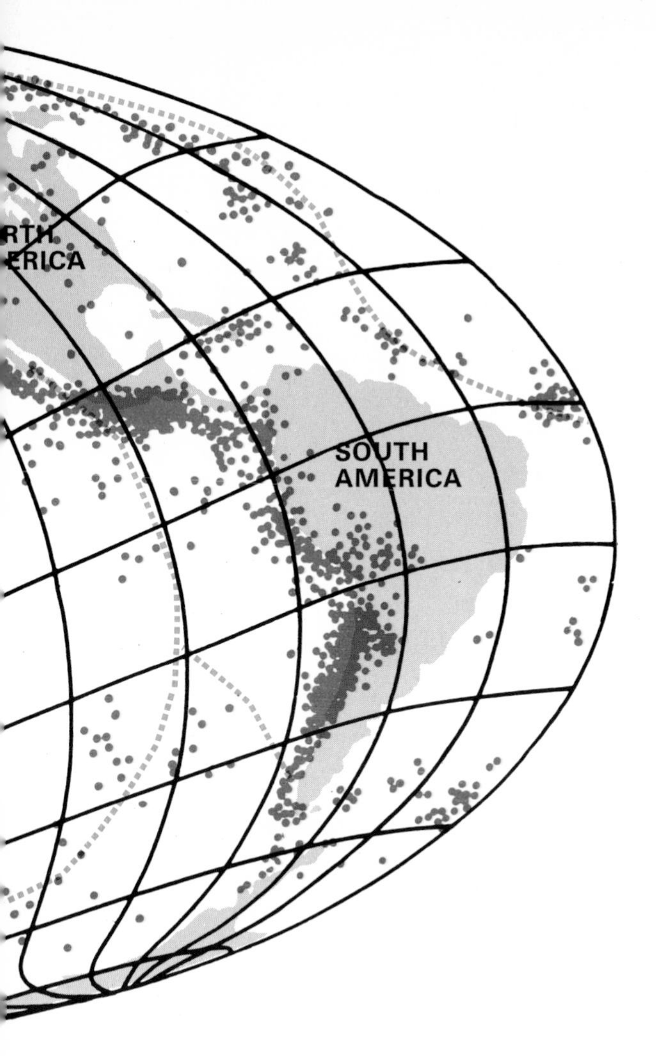

Where Earthquakes Occur

The clusters of dots on this map of the world show where major earthquakes have taken place over a period of 20 years. About 80 per cent of the quakes occur in a long belt around the rim of the Pacific Ocean. A second zone stretches from Spain across southern Europe and Asia to meet the Pacific group. A third belt runs under the oceans along a system of mountain ranges (*dotted line*) that indicate where land masses were once joined.

the Atlantic to the West Indies in a few hours. The quake occurred on the 1st of November—All Saints' Day—when the faithful all over Europe were in church. In the great cathedrals, awed spectators watched the chandeliers shake and swing to the shock waves from Lisbon.

The Lisbon quake was not the first by any means to have alarmed Europeans. But it was the most destructive by far, and the scale of the disaster reminded scientists how little they knew about the nature of earth tremors. One of them, the English astronomer-mathematician John Michell, collected all the reports he could find and was able to calculate that the shock wave had travelled at a speed of more than 20 miles a minute—1,200 miles an hour. Michell guessed that the source of the shock was an earth movement deep in the crust: ". . . it could not be much less than a mile or a mile and a half [deep]", he wrote, "and . . . it is probable that it did not exceed three miles".

Less than 30 years after the Lisbon disaster, a series of severe earthquakes convulsed the Calabrian district of southern Italy. The toll was far greater even than it had been in Lisbon—35,000 people lost their

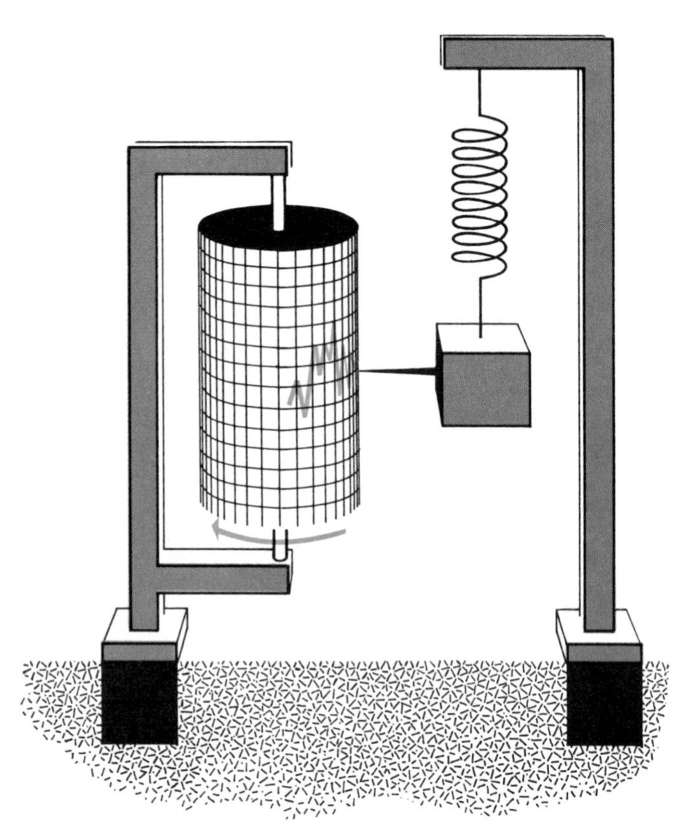

Tracing Quakes and Quivers

A seismograph, shown in simplified form in the drawing above, is an instrument that records the force and pattern of earthquakes. Its two metal frames are anchored solidly in rock. The frame at the left moves up and down with the earth's vibrations; at the same time its drum, fitted with graph paper, turns. Its movements are traced on the paper by the stylus, or pen, mounted on the heavy weight at the right; this does not move because the coil spring above it absorbs the shocks.

lives. This second disaster served to bring more and more scientific effort to bear on the earthquake question. An urgent need was felt for some accurate scientific instrument that would measure the upheavals. It seemed possible that some new apparatus would not only supply missing information about the earthquakes themselves but would also provide vital information about the earth's unknown interior.

In 1855—a century after the Lisbon tragedy—the first seismograph was built to record the force and pattern of earthquakes. Today hundreds of these instruments are at work around the world. No single seismograph can show the point at which an earthquake's tremors start. But each can tell the direction from which the tremors have come, and the distance away. Thus three seismographs at three different places can work together to pin-point the exact position of the earthquake's centre.

This new instrument soon showed that an earthquake shock is transmitted in several different forms. The slowest is called a surface wave; it travels like an ocean wave along the curve of the earth's thin crust. Other waves drive straight into the body of the earth at a speed much greater than that of the surface waves. These deeper waves are of two kinds, primary—or P—and secondary—or S—waves. P waves are the faster and more penetrating, moving easily through the dense matter of the earth's interior. The slower-moving S waves disappear when they encounter liquids.

At any seismograph station the first sign that an earthquake has occurred is the arrival of the P waves—the fastest ones. Later the S waves arrive. Still later, the slower surface waves, journeying along the crust of the earth, make their squiggle on the seismograph's revolving drum. In some cases, seismographs can also point to the source and indicate the force of a volcanic eruption or of a nuclear explosion.

Because these shock waves travel at different speeds as they move through different substances, scientists have been able to get a rough idea of what is inside the earth. They have learned, for example, that the earth's crust is an average of 20 miles thick beneath the continents. Under the oceans, however, the crust is only about three miles thick.

The next layer towards the earth's centre is known as the mantle. Where the crust ends and the mantle begins, the shock waves from earthquakes suddenly speed up. This increase in speed grows as the waves travel ever deeper into the mantle. But at a point 1,800 miles below the surface of the earth, another abrupt change takes place. The faster P waves speed up even more, and the S waves simply disappear. This is the region known as the core, and scientists believe it consists of liquid iron. There are three basic reasons to think that this is so. For one thing, it is known that S waves cannot travel through a liquid. Thus, the fact that they disappear when they travel below

E Marks the Earthquake

Seismographs in different cities are used together to pin-point the exact centre of an earthquake. Each instrument records the arrival of the vibrations that travel out from a quake. By measuring the time lapse between the primary and secondary shock waves, seismologists are able to estimate the distance travelled. Next, a circle with the distance as its radius is drawn around each city on a map. The single point at which all three circles cross is the earthquake's exact position or "epicentre" (E).

1,800 miles indicates that they have reached a liquid.

The second reason is that, to account for the total weight of the earth, the core must be composed of a heavy metal—iron. Further, the iron must be enormously compressed. In fact it is estimated that the iron in the earth's core weighs 750 pounds per cubic foot. The same amount of iron on the earth's surface weighs 250 pounds less.

The core must also be very hot. Most scientists today think that its temperature is somewhere between 2,000 and 4,500 degrees centigrade. But with nearly 2,000 miles of insulating rock between the core and the surface, the heat is contained deep within the earth.

The third, and perhaps the most important reason, is based on evidence that has been found in meteorites. Most meteorites contain a great deal of metallic iron; some, in fact, are almost totally composed of iron. Meteors are a part of the solar system, and were probably formed in the same way as the planets (although on a much smaller scale), and of the same materials. Therefore, scientists reason, if meteorites contain large amounts of metallic iron, so must the earth and the other planets.

Man will probably never be able to visit these strange regions deep inside his planet. Sending men to the moon or even to the other planets is a far simpler task. But we may soon know what lies just beneath the earth's crust, in the upper part of the mantle. Because the crust is only three miles thick at the ocean floor, scientists hope to drill through the sea bottom to reach the mantle. In one U.S. attempt to do this, called Project Mohole, drills were sent through two miles of ocean water to make test holes one-fifth of a mile into the crust.

The more man discovers about the interior the more will he be able to learn about the origins of the earth, and even of the entire solar system. But there is another reason why scientists are anxious to know what is in the interior of this planet. They hope to find out how the earth's magnetic field works.

The magnetic compass has been used by sailors for nearly a thousand years. At first many people thought that its needle was attracted by the constellation known as the Great Bear, or perhaps Polaris, the North Star. Some even thought that a huge mountain caused the needle to point north. But in the year 1600 an Englishman named William Gilbert showed that the earth itself acted as a huge magnet.

Scientists now believe that the earth's magnetism is generated by the swirling of the molten iron that they think forms the core of the planet. This theory provides yet another reason to think that the core is indeed a hot mass of liquid metal.

The earth's magnetic field is strange and unpredictable, however. For one thing, the north magnetic pole moves. Not only is it several hundred miles from the true North Pole, but in the last half-century it has

Damage from Shifting Rock

Earthquakes occur when movement in the plastic upper mantle causes the more brittle surface rock to break. One section of the crust shifts in relation to another—which is what happened under a once-straight railway track in California (*left*). Such events produce powerful shock waves. These shake the earth and may cause buildings to lurch or topple and fires to break out, as they did during a severe earthquake in 1948 in Fukui, Japan (*below*).

moved 270 miles to the north-west. And the magnetic field does not have a constant strength. In fact, it has been growing weaker—in the last 100 years its power has decreased by 5 per cent.

There is recent evidence that the earth's magnetic field undergoes even more startling changes. According to one theory, the field periodically reverses itself—the north and south magnetic poles exchange places. These reversals have occurred at a rate of about two every million years.

The evidence to support this theory has been found in iron-bearing rocks in the earth's crust. Because the atoms in iron molecules act as tiny magnets, the iron in these rocks becomes aligned in the direction of the field when the rocks are being formed. When the magnetic poles shift, the atoms remain pointing, like arrows, towards the earlier pole. By determining the age of these rocks, geologists can determine when the poles exchange places.

What happens when the magnetic poles reverse? Compasses, of course, will continue to point to the north magnetic pole, wherever it is—even if it is situated in Antarctica, at the geographic South Pole. But the earth's magnetic field does not only serve as a handy guide for mariners and explorers. It is also responsible for shielding the earth from bombardment by cosmic rays and particles emitted by the sun and other stars. If the magnetic field weakens, more of this radiation can get through to

Slicing Life of Long Ago

Land under the ocean floor contains fossils that help us to understand the history of life on earth. The long cylinder in the picture above is a core of clay brought up from hundreds of feet under the water. A palaeontologist is slicing the core into sections, so that the fossils can be removed and studied.

Measuring Earthly Tides

The earth's crust, in addition to cracking in earthquakes, is constantly stretching and tightening up, because the moon's attraction creates "tides" on solid land as well as on oceans. The instrument shown here, called a strain meter, measures these movements deep inside a mountain.

reach the earth's surface. And scientists believe that in the process of reversing itself the field is weakened—for just how long is not yet known.

Even with a strong magnetic field, all radiation is not prevented from reaching the earth. The plants and animals—including man—that now live on the earth have adapted to this radiation. But what would happen to living things if the radiation were to increase? An overdose of charged particles, for example, can damage living cells. If reproductive cells are damaged, the genetic structure of those cells—which determines heredity—may be altered in a process known as mutation.

Scientists have searched for evidence of such an evolutionary change, evidence that would indicate great numbers of mutations at the times the magnetic field changed. So far they have found none, and recent estimates indicate that if such an increase in radiation does occur it is probably slight. One scientist has likened the difference to that of moving from Marseilles to Grenoble. That is, from a city at sea level to one whose altitude is one mile. Grenoble's residents are shielded by one mile less atmosphere than Marseilles'—yet no one has found that mutations occur more often in Grenoble.

But scientists have made an interesting discovery involving plankton, a tiny, simple form of animal life that lives in oceans. By digging into the sea floor and obtaining fossils of plankton they have found that at exactly the point in time when the magnetic field reversed itself, older types of plankton seemed to die out, to be replaced by newer types. There is no clear-cut explanation for this sudden change. But the fact that it has occurred indicates that there may be a connection between the changing forms of plankton and the shift in the magnetic field.

What force causes these mysterious shifts in the earth's magnetic field? Only recently it was discovered that 700,000 years ago—exactly when the last reversal took place—a gigantic meteor hit the continent of Antarctica. And 300,000 years before that, when the magnetic field was reversed, a huge meteor plunged into Africa. These two occurrences may merely be coincidences; scientists do not yet know the answer.

A Crack that Means Danger

The dark line in this aerial photograph is a part of the 600-mile-long San Andreas fault, a large crack in the earth in California. The land to the east (*right*) is inching southwards. The strain created eventually makes the surface crack, causing an earthquake like the one in San Francisco in 1906.

TOWERING THUNDERCLOUDS pour rain into the Pacific Ocean off the island of Samoa. The lowest clouds, from which the rain seems to be falling, are only the very bottom of the heap; thunderstorms like this one often extend from just above the ocean to an altitude of more than eight miles.

3
The Mighty Engine of the Atmosphere

The sea, which covers nearly three-quarters of the globe, is only the second biggest thing on earth. Much larger is the ocean of the atmosphere, which dominates the lives of men and all other creatures as surely as water dominates the lives of fish. Without the atmosphere's oxygen living things die almost at once. Without rain erosion and the weathering of rocks there

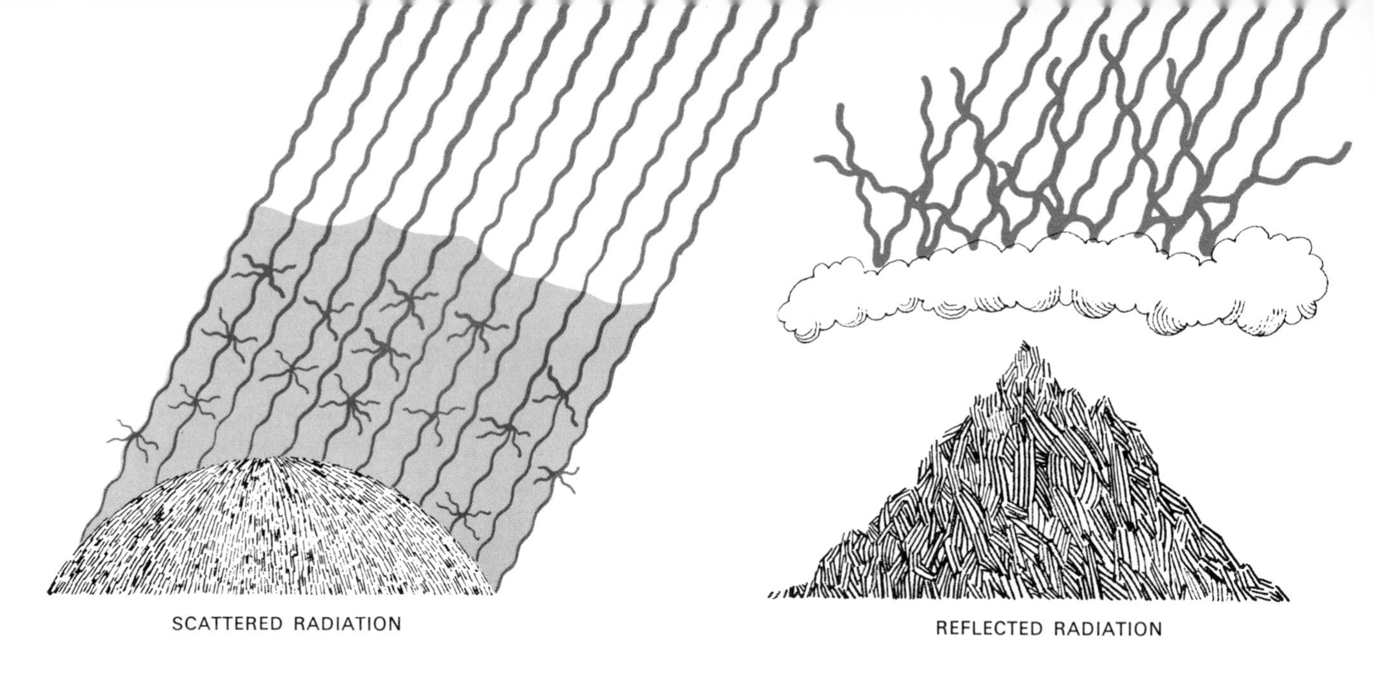

SCATTERED RADIATION

REFLECTED RADIATION

would be no soil for plants to grow in. Without carbon dioxide the plants could not produce carbohydrates, the primary link in the food chain that supports all animal life. Without the high-altitude umbrella of ozone to absorb the deadly ultra-violet rays of the sun, human existence—if any—would be quite different. Yet this is only a small list of the free services performed by the atmosphere and taken for granted by more that 3,000 million human beings who at this moment are drawing breaths of it.

The atmosphere is an invisible mixture of gases—nitrogen, oxygen, carbon dioxide and water vapour make up most of the ocean of air. It also contains dust particles and the waste products of men, such as soot and radioactive fall-out particles from nuclear explosions. At sea level a cubic foot of this mixture weighs about an ounce and a quarter, but because of the force with which gravity holds it in place, the atmosphere exerts a pressure of about 15 pounds per square inch at sea level. The human body and, of course, animals and plants balance this pressure by exerting an equal outward pressure. Just as water pressure is greatest at the bottom of the sea, so atmospheric pressure is greatest at the bottom of the ocean of air. The greater the altitude the less the pressure, and the thinner the atmosphere becomes. The ocean of air is dense enough at a height of 12 miles to support aeroplanes and balloons. It continues to thin out at higher altitudes until at a point many hundreds of miles above the earth's surface it blends with the almost total emptiness of space.

Meteorologists, the scientists who study the atmosphere and its weather patterns, have found that the atmosphere is divided into five basic parts. They are known as the troposphere, the stratosphere, the mesosphere, the ionosphere and the exosphere. The troposphere is the bottom layer, and it supports all life. Its upper boundary is as low as 5 miles above the North and South Poles, as high as 10 miles above the equator. Everywhere within the troposphere

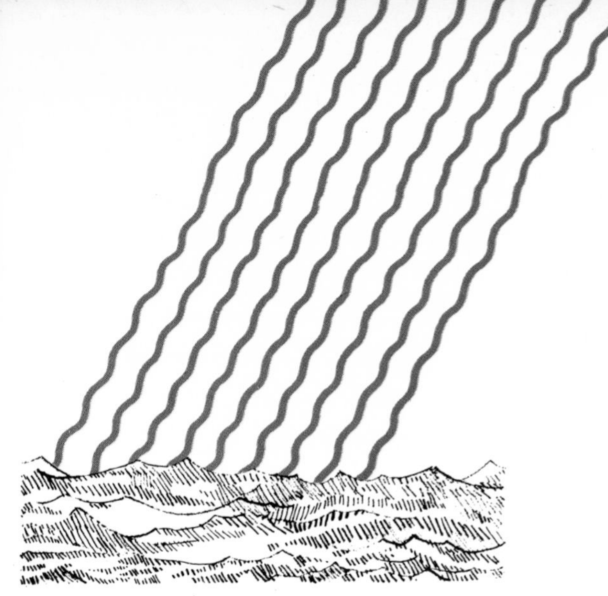

Sun Power to Run the Earth

Of the sun's total radiation, only a small fraction is aimed at the earth. But that amount is more than enough to keep our planet running. Some of the radiation is scattered by air, dust and water vapour in the atmosphere (*far left*). Clouds reflect about 25 per cent of the radiation (*centre*). The remainder (*left*) heats the earth's surface, which in turn re-radiates the energy to heat the atmosphere and thus run the world's vast weather machine.

the air is a constant mixture: nitrogen 78 per cent, oxygen 21 per cent, argon 0.9 per cent, carbon dioxide 0.03 per cent—with traces of half a dozen other gases plus a variable amount of water vapour.

Starting in the stratosphere, a layer extending 10 to 15 miles higher, and in the mesosphere, which goes up to the 50-mile level, there are important chemical changes in the air. In the stratosphere, ozone is added to the mixture. This gas, an uncommon form of oxygen, is generated when an electrical discharge or strong ultra-violet rays pass through ordinary oxygen. In the upper atmosphere, ozone soaks up much of the ultra-violet radiation streaming earthwards from the sun.

Starting at 50 miles above the earth and reaching to from 350 to 600 miles is the ionosphere, in which rays from the sun ionize the air, producing electrically charged atoms and molecules. The air in the ionosphere is terribly thin, but it is this layer that reflects radio waves back to earth, making possible long-distance broadcasts. Where the ionosphere ends, the exosphere begins. Although it is a part of our atmosphere, it is not composed of air as we know it. The inner portion of the exosphere is a 900-mile-thick layer of helium, the same gas that is used to inflate the toy balloons youngsters clamour for in parks and at circuses. Beyond the helium is the outer part of the exosphere, a layer of hydrogen. Both the helium and hydrogen layers are extremely rarefied—so much so that individual molecules, which bump into one another frequently at sea level, seldom even come in contact with one another. And beyond the thin exosphere, some 5,500 miles from the surface of the earth, there is no more atmosphere. At 5,500 miles space begins.

From this quick tour, working from the inside out, it is apparent that the atmosphere is a very important part of the earth. Its major action is to serve as an enormous engine, using the sun's radiation as a power source to drive the currents of air that stream and eddy around the earth.

Although it is the sun's power that runs the atmospheric engine, the power is not applied directly. The sun does not heat the air. In fact, much of the radiation from the sun—the radiation we see as light and feel as heat—passes right through the air, striking and warming the planet's surface. It is the earth itself that heats the air from below, in much the same way as a pot of water is heated over the flames of the stove.

The earth's surface is not warmed the same amount everywhere by the sun's rays. Sunlight strikes the earth more directly at the equator than it does at the Poles, so the air near the equator is warmer than the air to the north or south. It is this difference in the temperature of the air that turns the atmosphere into an engine: the warm air, being lighter, rises, while the heavier cold air moves in to take its place, causing the winds to blow.

If the earth did not rotate, these air cur-

A Cold Front Barges In

Forcing its way beneath a mass of warm light air, a cool, heavier air mass travels from left to right in the illustration below. Because it is lighter, the warmer air is pushed upwards by the cooler air. As it rises, the warm air cools and the water vapour it contains condenses to form thunderclouds and rain, which occur along the cold front.

rents would be quite orderly: warm air near the equator would rise and flow towards the Poles, while cold air at the Poles would sink and flow towards the equator in an endless cycle. The earth's rotation modifies this simple pattern: in each hemisphere, working away from the Pole and towards the equator, there is first a westward drift of air in the lower atmosphere, then an eastward one in mid-latitudes, and finally another westward drift near the equator. The pattern of air flow in each hemisphere is a mirror image of the pattern in the other: the easterly winds of the northern tropics—the "trade winds"—blow from the north-east, while the same easterly trades below the equator blow from the south-east. The name trade wind originated in the days of sailing ships, when these steady winds were the mainstay of ocean commerce.

The westerly winds of middle latitudes do not share the trade winds' regular, stable pattern. Instead, they are rolled into im-

A Warm Front Creeps Up

Like a cold front, a warm front often brings rain. But while the arrival of a cold front with its wall of thunder-clouds is dramatic, the arrival of a warm front is quiet and relatively gentle. The lighter, warmer air slides up over the cool air mass, causing rain, and forming wispy, high-altitude clouds that may appear several days before the front arrives.

New York Masked in Haze . . .

Warm, moist tropical air, which has moved in from the Atlantic Ocean to the south, combines with New York's smoke to form a thick blanket of "smaze", as a mixture of smoke and haze is sometimes called. This photograph was taken from a skyscraper on 50th Street. The Empire State Building, only 16 blocks away, can barely be seen.

mense high-altitude eddies, thousands of miles across. Below these large-scale eddies (three to six of which are over each hemisphere at any one time) are many smaller ones that swirl about for a few hours or days before they vanish and are replaced by others. The larger eddies are more persistent: one of them may move eastwards for weeks before breaking up. The birth and growth of these wind swirls account for the changeable weather of the earth's middle latitudes.

A smaller eddy that forms around a centre of low-pressure air acquires a rotary motion and starts to spin—counterclockwise in the Northern Hemisphere and clockwise south of the equator. Such a spinning eddy is called a cyclone, but is not necessarily the storm wind that is sometimes known

by the same name. Here is a chance to watch the atmosphere's heat engine in action on a small scale. Why does a cyclone spin? The air at its centre is lighter and lower in pressure while the air surrounding the eddy is heavier and higher in pressure. Thus, the heavier air flows *inwards*, towards the centre, and it is this inward flow that is deflected by the rotation of the earth. Consider the opposite case: the eddy forms around a deep, dense air mass at higher pressure than the air around it, and the air flow is therefore directed *outwards* from its centre. In consequence, the spin is in exactly the opposite direction and such an eddy is known as an anticyclone.

These great whorls of air make the major marks on weather maps. The United States is often swept in winter by high-pressure

. . . Reappears When It Clears

A mass of cool, dry polar air has moved in from the north, pushing the unpleasant smaze before it, and the view is now measured in miles rather than blocks. But the cooler air does not always arrive immediately; New York and other industrialized, smoke-producing cities are often bathed for days at a time in the fumes of their own air pollution.

CIRRUS: 20,000 TO 40,000 FEET

CIRROCUMULUS: 20,000 TO 40,000 FEET

CUMULUS: 8,000 FEET TO 45,000 FEET FROM BASE TO TOP

The Language of Clouds

For thousands of years men have "read" clouds for signs of changing weather. The three basic types of clouds are *cirrus* (Latin for "curl of hair"), *cumulus* ("pile") and *stratus* ("spread out"). Among the highest clouds (*top row*) are *cirrus*, whose wisps of tiny ice crystals indicate a far-off storm. *Cirrocumulus*, sometimes called a "mackerel sky", herald a cold front; *cirrostratus*, seen as a halo around the sun, mean that rain is likely. At middle altitudes float the puffy *cumulus*, which may grow into *cumulonimbus*, or "thunderheads". Still lower, *altocumulus* may be a sign of rain and *altostratus* often indicate prolonged rain or snow. The lowest clouds (*bottom row*) include the thick, dark *nimbostratus*, which bring continuous rain or snow; the flat, grey *stratus*, which are accompanied by a drizzle or snow flurries; and the wavy *stratocumulus*, which may drop a light sprinkling of snow.

ALTOCUMULUS: 8,000 TO 20,000 FEET

NIMBOSTRATUS: BELOW 8,000 FEET

STRATUS: BELOW 8,000 FEET

CIRROSTRATUS: 20,000 TO 40,000 FEET

CUMULONIMBUS: 10,000 TO 60,000 FEET FROM BASE TO TOP

ALTOSTRATUS: 8,000 TO 20,000 FEET

STRATOCUMULUS: BELOW 8,000 FEET

systems from northern Canada that are very cold and dry. When such a cold air mass overlies a region, the weather will be cold and clear. In summer, moist lows from the Gulf of Mexico often dominate weather in the eastern United States, producing hot, humid, windless days.

The line of contact between two air masses of different temperature is called a "front". A cold front represents cold air replacing warmer air; a warm front moves in such a way that warm air replaces cold. The warm air along a front of either kind cools as it rises, producing cloudiness and precipitation. This effect is more noticeable along a cold front, which usually leads to more violent storms. The approach and passage of a front is signalled by cirrus clouds—"mare's-tails"—high in the sky. Soon a milky film of cirrostratus covers the sky, and some hours later the ominous grey veils of altostratus clouds appear. Then low, thick, dark nimbostratus clouds darken the sky and rain begins to fall. Finally the warm air completely replaces the cold, from top to bottom, the temperature levels off and the rain stops. More or less steady weather then follows until the approach of the next front.

The sequence of events when a cold front arrives is faster and often more dramatic. The cold oncoming air is too heavy to override the warm air in its path, and burrows underneath instead. Forced upwards by the cold air mass, the warm moisture-laden air

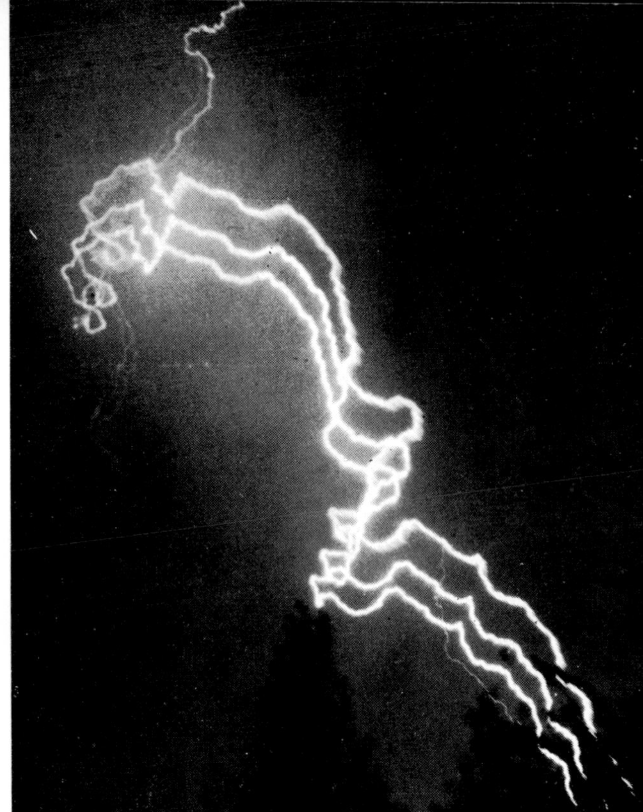

condenses, forming a great vertical bank of dense cumulonimbus clouds. A well-defined cold front usually appears as a squall line of dark clouds, straight as a ruler from horizon to horizon, sweeping in from the west or north-west. When it strikes, the wind shifts abruptly from south-west to north-west, the temperature falls and a torrent of heavy rain begins, driven by strong, irregular gusts. A violent thunderstorm may occur, adding sight and sound to the tempestuous proceedings. After half an hour or so the squall line is almost out of sight to the east, and a band of clear sky appears in the west. Then the north-west wind blows more steadily, and dry, cool, clear weather sets in. Of course, not all cold fronts bring with them such boisterous effects, but the pattern is familiar to dwellers in the middle latitudes.

The turbulent, unstable atmosphere near a squall line sometimes produces a vortex of rapidly spinning air. The vortex appears as a narrow, funnel-shaped cloud that extends to the ground and conceals winds of hundreds of miles an hour. A vortex of this kind is called a tornado on land and a water-spout over the ocean. Very little is known about conditions inside the whirlwinds, because any instruments that have happened to be in their paths have always been destroyed.

Few people have looked such a whirlwind in the "eye" and lived to tell about it. One who did was Will Keller, a Kansas farmer who dared to peek out of his storm cellar as a tornado passed over in 1928. Above him was the hollow vortex, 50 to 100 feet across, its walls lighted by zigzag lightning flashes. Smaller vortexes were forming inside the main one and emitting

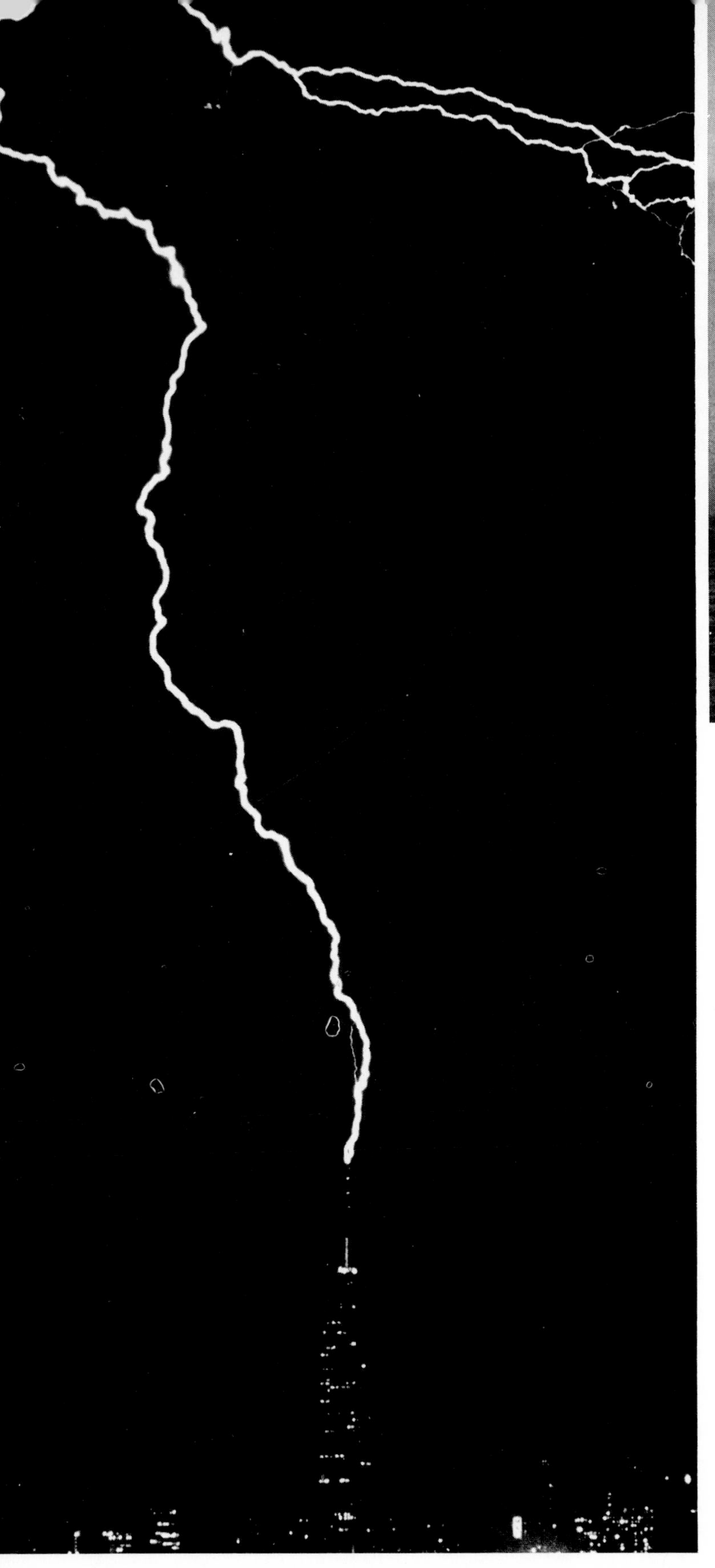

When Lightning Strikes

Lightning occurs when there is enough difference in the electrical charge of clouds and earth for a "spark" to jump the gap. On the far left, the sky, as seen from a forest ranger's tower, is filled with a series of lightning flashes. Next to this is a picture showing a triple stroke made by flashes only fractions of a second apart. Lightning is usually attracted to the tallest object in the area. One of the hundreds of lightning bolts that strike the Empire State Building harmlessly each year is shown on the left; above, a bolt is even attracted to a tower of water thrown up by the explosion of a Navy depth charge.

hissing noises as they broke free of it.

Usually a tornado is a few hundred yards across and travels at perhaps 25 miles an hour for a distance of anywhere from a fraction of a mile to 100 miles or more before it vanishes. The central United States probably has more tornadoes than any other part of the world, and they form so rapidly and unpredictably that about the only protection against them is to climb into a strong storm cellar whenever a thunderstorm appears. Water-spouts are generally milder than tornadoes, though still capable of violent destruction. The lower portion of a spout contains some salt water drawn up from the sea beneath it, but consists mostly of fresh water that has condensed out from its basic body of cloud. Some water-spouts range up to a mile in height.

Many places have other peculiar winds of their own that are more or less unrelated to the global pattern. Simple examples are the sea and land breezes familiar along many coast lines. These winds owe their existence to the fact that the temperature of the ocean surface stays fairly constant while that of the land surface may fluctuate widely. On a hot day a beach becomes warm and the air above it rises while cooler, denser air from over the water—the sea breeze—is drawn in to replace it. At night the beach cools rapidly and the air circulation is reversed: the air over the land is now denser, and a land breeze flows off shore.

The sea and land breezes' grown-up relatives are the monsoons of Asia, which are

A Twister's Fearful Path

A tornado thunders down a Texas highway. Wherever its whirling tip touches down, it leaves destruction; bits of houses, which have been pulled apart and flung into the air, are visible in the photograph above. The damage a twister does is often freakish. It may level an entire city block, yet leave one house standing. Or, as in the case of the Iowa farmyard on the right, it can destroy a barn, tear the top from a silo—and leave five horses unhurt, still standing in the wreckage of their stalls.

governed by the contrasts in land and sea temperatures in summer and winter, instead of in daytime and night-time. In winter the Asiatic plateau is bitterly cold, so that the overlying air is much denser than that above the China Sea and the Indian Ocean to its east and south. A steady cold, dry wind blows off shore from October to April, deflected by the earth's rotation into a north-east wind in the China Sea and in the northern part of the Indian Ocean. In the summer, Asia swelters and the air above it rises, while cooler air moves in from the ocean. This summer "monsoon" brings air that has picked up a considerable amount of moisture as it crossed the sea, and its arrival deluges South-East Asia with prolonged, drenching rain. A monsoon climate of this kind has only two varieties of weather, wet in summer and dry in winter, in contrast to the changing weather of middle-latitude weather.

Other regional winds are conditioned by landscape as well as temperature. Cold, dry air may spill over a mountain range suddenly after having collected on the windward side of the range for some time, surging down into adjacent valleys with great force. The "mistral", a French wind, consists of cold air from the Rhone Glacier that pours down the valley of the river Rhone to the sea for much of the year, while the "bora" of the Adriatic Sea has a similar birth in the mountains of Yugoslavia. The geography of the Mediterranean, bordered by high mountains on the north and the hot Sahara on the south, is responsible for a number of notorious winds. At times a hot wind from the Sahara, the "sirocco", blows north across the Mediterranean, accumulating enough water vapour to bring rain to Sicily and the Italian coast.

Those who live along the fringes of the world's oceans have good reason to fear the coming of autumn, when tropical cyclones are most likely to be born at sea and to cause disaster if they sweep over the land. The western shores of the North Atlantic, the North and South Pacific, and the Indian Oceans are most often the targets of tropical cyclones. They are unknown only in the South Atlantic and in the eastern part of the South Pacific. These violent tropical storms are quite rare (only an average of 48 occur each year in the entire world), but their high power sets them apart, along with earthquakes, as the most destructive of natural phenomena.

At birth, one of these typhoons or hurricanes forms as a zone of low atmospheric pressure over a tropical ocean. Warm air laden with moisture flows towards this zone and rises within it. The water vapour in the rising column of warm air condenses into clouds and rain, freeing a great deal of heat in the process, which further speeds the upward flow of air. Perhaps a quarter of a million tons of water are extracted from the ocean and the air every *second* by a hurricane, and their condensation over

Tracking a Hurricane

From high above the earth the travels of a hurricane are closely watched. A weather satellite streaking over the southern United States took the photograph on the right, which was relayed to the ground by radio. The outline of the Florida coast line placed over the picture shows the centre of the storm to be north of Jacksonville. A radar installation at Miami also tracked the hurricane (*above*). Miami is at the centre of the radar screen, and the calm, cloudless "eye" of the storm is about 75 miles to the north of the city.

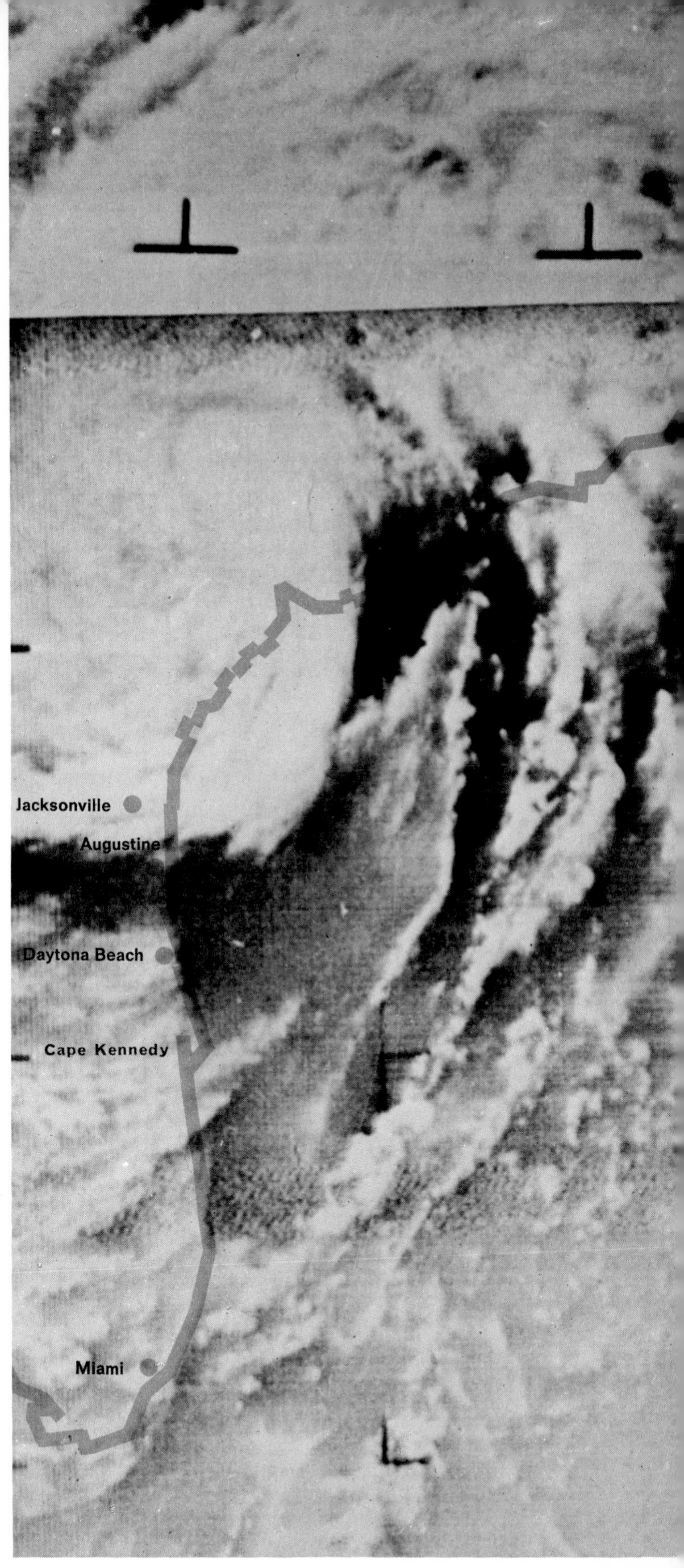

one day releases energy equivalent to the explosion of an 11,500-megaton nuclear bomb. As the heated air rises faster and faster, new air converges on the storm centre with ever increasing speed; winds of as much as 200 miles an hour may be generated in this way.

The hurricane itself is a nightmare of shrieking wind accompanied by torrents of rain and darkness, as dense clouds blot out the sky. If the "eye" passes overhead, the turmoil becomes increasingly louder, then abruptly stops; the wind falls to a breeze, the rain ceases and bits of blue sky appear through thin, patchy clouds. But the lull is brief and soon the full fury of the storm

strikes again, now with the wind from the opposite direction.

Such a storm is fuelled by the heat and water vapour that it sucks up from the surface of the sea, and it weakens and disappears in quick time when it is deprived of this power supply. Thus hurricanes seldom penetrate far inland, and if they miss land

A Storm Hits Cape Cod

Huge seas, raised by an ocean storm, batter the waterfront of Provincetown, Massachusetts, at the tip of Cape Cod on the U.S. Atlantic coast. Every year the cape is beset by such storms, which slowly wear away the sand dunes facing the Atlantic. The same storms add sand to the side that faces sheltered Cape Cod Bay.

entirely by swinging towards the Pole, the colder water in their paths quenches their violence before long.

In a single year the engine of the atmosphere, using such forceful instruments as typhoons and monsoons and such peaceful ones as sunlight, lifts 100,000 cubic miles of water into the air from the sea and the continents. Everything that goes up in this massive evaporation process must eventually come down, and most of it precipitates as rain.

In order for rain, snow, sleet or hail to fall, clouds must form. Even air that is supersaturated with moisture cannot usually produce clouds unless countless numbers of tiny "condensation nuclei" are present. The nuclei may be particles of salt from sea spray, or fine dust, or smoke particles from forest fires and industrial plants, or the combustion products of volcanoes. It has been estimated that the eruption in 1883 on the volcanic island of Krakatoa, in the Indonesian archipelago, filled the atmosphere with enough condensation nuclei to provide 1,000 rainy days throughout the world.

The water-vapour molecules that join a nucleus form cloud droplets (or ice crystals, if the air is well below freezing). These cannot fall as rain: they hold only a millionth as much water as an ordinary raindrop. In absolutely still air they would take eight hours to fall a quarter of a mile, and in moving air they are hardly affected by gravity at all. It is their growth to bigger size that makes precipitation possible. In turbulent air bigger droplets collide with and "collect" smaller ones; in cold air, droplets evaporate and then condense on near-by ice crystals.

Only when a droplet grows to raindrop size, at least 1/125th of an inch in diameter, can it fall out of the cloud. It may never reach the ground; often a torrent may spill out of clouds high above a desert, only to evaporate entirely on the way down. Raindrops that reach the earth in a fine spray, called drizzle, have fallen from relatively low clouds, with little time to collide with other drops while falling. The raindrops that arrive in a vigorous downpour come from deep clouds where the colliding of droplets, and the "capturing" of little ones by bigger ones, is going on quite actively.

A Fountain of Colour

The thunderstorm is almost over in the Arizona desert. Suddenly the lingering grey clouds part, and the afternoon sunlight streams forth. As the bright rays shine through the last of the rain, each drop acts as a prism, splitting the white light into every colour of the spectrum, signalling the storm's end.

4

Erosion: Forces That Shape the Land

It is not every day that a new-born volcano shoots lava out of a cornfield or an island sinks beneath the waves or an earthquake crumbles a city. While the earth is always rearranging its features, most of its changes of face are leisurely rather than catastrophic. A human lifetime simply does not offer a long enough look to make most of the changes apparent. So until a few generations ago most people assumed that the landscape was here to stay. The hills were thought to be eternal, or, as the 19th-century American poet, William Cullen Bryant, put it, "ancient as the sun".

But 19th-century geologists were already taking closer looks at the earth around them and beginning to find clues that had been available all along. Shore lines everywhere were advancing or retreating; the brink of Niagara Falls was receding a few feet every year; some "eternal" hills were

THE BADLANDS of South Dakota in the U.S. South-West are a spectacular result of erosion, Nature's tool for carving and flattening the face of the earth. The jagged, crumpled landscape of clay and sandstone was once a smooth, sloping plain that lay between the Rocky Mountains and the Great Plains of the Midwest.

1. RAINWATER

2. ACIDS FROM LICHENS

3. WIND FROST AND RAIN

decaying while others appeared to be on the rise. In time it was realized that even the splash of a single raindrop on the soil counted for something in the remoulding of the earth.

During this reappraisal of the landscape the ruins of the Greek temple of Serapis at Pozzuoli, near Naples, were excavated. When this building was studied by scientists, it was found that several of its columns were still standing upright and that three of them were riddled with holes drilled by a species of borer clam that is still common in the near-by Mediterranean. What was puzzling was that some of these holes were bored near the tops of the columns, and there was no known way that clams could have climbed up there. The mystery was not settled until men finally believed what the evidence clearly showed: the temple had been engulfed by the sea when the land under it sank. The borer clams did their work, and later on the temple rose again, its columns still upright.

Nothing else on the face of the globe, it turns out, is unchangeable either. For two major sets of forces are engaged in a titanic contest, of which the pioneer Scottish geologist James Hutton said: "We find no sign of a beginning—no prospect of an end". These are the tearing-down forces of weathering and erosion and the uplifting forces that begin deep within the earth.

Weathering and erosion include all the processes by which rock is worn away and its debris deposited somewhere else. The uplifting forces are called diastrophism, from the Greek meaning "thorough turning over". It refers to the processes by which

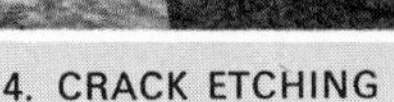

4. CRACK ETCHING

5. FROST

6. SANDBLASTING

the earth's crust is uplifted, tilted, fractured and folded and dragged down from below. If either erosion or diastrophism ever gained full power, this would become an unrecognizable world. Erosion would wash most of North America into the oceans within 25 million years, leaving only a wide, low plain, which might ultimately be entirely covered by the sea. Diastrophism would contort the earth's surface into contours as jagged as the mountains of the moon. Such things do not happen, because a balance of power exists between erosion and diastrophism, although it is far from peaceful.

Once the nature of the struggle between the two forces of erosion and diastrophism was understood, scientists were able to clear up most of the mystery of the earth's topography. The jumbled rocks were given meaning and could be understood.

Many Kinds of Weathering

Weather changes the earth's landscape by tearing down rock in various ways, some of which are shown here. *(1)* Rainwater made vertical cracks deeper and deeper in limestone rock to carve the spectacular pillars of Utah's Bryce Canyon in America's mountainous West. *(2)* Acids, manufactured by red lichen plants, have eaten into a volcanic rock. *(3)* Wind-driven sand, frost and rainwater all helped to model this strange stone sculpture in Utah. *(4)* Heat and moisture have eroded the original cracks of a large block of granite into horizontal segments that were eventually worn into a smooth rock stack. *(5)* Water in cracks of rock froze and expanded, loosening chunks from a cliff face. *(6)* Sand-laden wind in the Sahara desert in Africa blasted this soft rock into weird forms.

The sources of the great heavings that lift up the mountains are deeply hidden from view. But most of the agents of erosion work openly for all to see. The greatest of these is running water. The atmosphere sucks up about 100,000 cubic miles of moisture every year. Most of this falls back into the oceans, but about 35,000 cubic miles of it reaches the land as rain, snow, sleet, hail and dew. A great deal of this water goes underground, and a great deal more evaporates again before flowing very far, but an estimated 8,000 million million gallons run off to resupply the seas. This is the flood that year after year does the most to reshape the land.

It is not so much the water itself that does the work, but the particles and chemicals that it carries along. The change in colour from a clear, swift mountain stream to the slow, brown currents of a major river shows how each tributary adds its portion of particles to the main stream's load. The river Mississippi system, for example, drains an area of about a million and a quarter square miles. In a year, something like 500 million tons of mud, clay, mineral fragments and pinpoint-sized lumps of rock are carried down and dropped into the Gulf of Mexico. From the first flake of mica swirling in a mountain brook to the last quartz sand grain stripped from a downstream bar, each particle serves as one of the Mississippi system's erosive teeth, nibbling at river-banks and bottoms along the way.

The speed of flow of water is a vital factor in the erosive power of streams. A youthful, steep mountain torrent, flowing about 10 feet a second, not only carries fine particles in suspension and mineral salts in solution, but also rolls, pushes and tumbles masses of pebbles, gravel and even boulders downhill along its bed. As the gradient levels off and the water loses velocity, the larger stones are left behind, then the smaller ones. A stream is a kind of sorting machine, grading its suspended load with fair precision. Coarse materials fall out first, gravels and sand reaching the bottom and the banks long before the finer fragments of mud can sink.

Most often a great river valley begins as tiny channels in the soft surfaces of hill-sides. With each rainfall the channels are deepened by run-off water until they become gullies. The stream always follows the shortest and easiest path downhill. As it grows bigger, the stream can carry more and more grinding materials and its cutting force increases.

In time the rapids and waterfalls of the young river eat away the irregularities in its bed, and the resulting gentler slope reduces the current's vigour. As they age, streams that were once swift and straight broaden out their narrow, steep-sided valleys. They turn into old rivers like the Yellow and the Mississippi, meandering sluggishly across broad valleys. These valleys are smooth and flat because of the burden of mud and silt distributed by the

A Plateau's Eventful Past

A "stairway" of eroded land in the Colorado Plateau shows different ages of rock, from the youngest layer at Bryce Canyon to the oldest at the bottom of the Grand Canyon. After the pre-Cambrian period (*bottom layer*), warm, shallow seas repeatedly covered the area, disappearing and returning. These seas deposited layers of hard-packed sand and mud on the lowest bedrock. About 10 million years ago, some mighty force raised the entire area thousands of feet above sea level. Since then, rains and rivers have gradually exposed the rock as they chiselled the landscape into the formations that we see today.

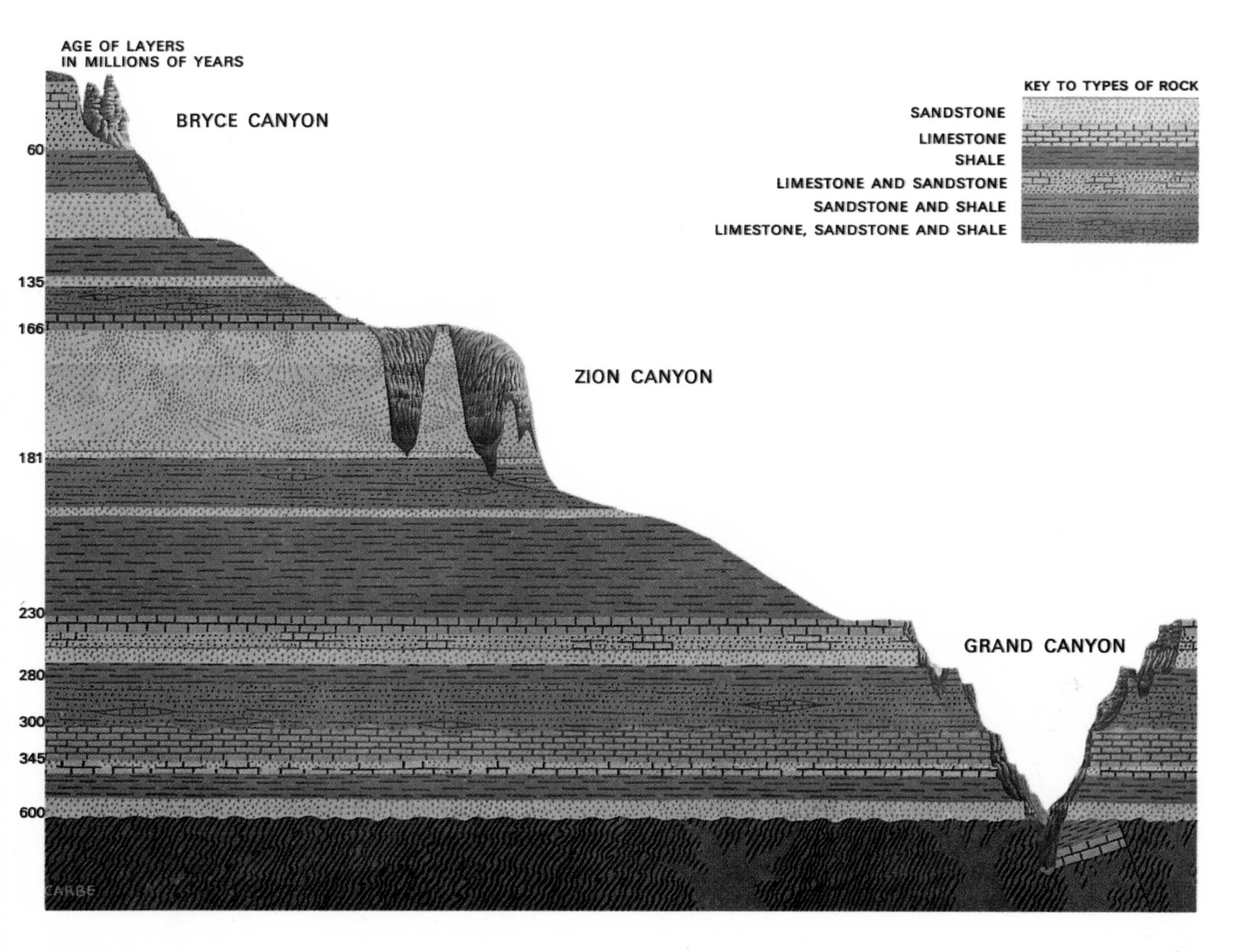

Carving a Limestone Cave

Eerie caves like the Carlsbad Caverns in New Mexico (*left*) are formed by the erosion process shown in these sketches. In the sketch above, water containing carbonic acid has seeped down through large cracks in porous limestone rock. Blocked by less porous rock under the limestone, the water eats its way horizontally, reaching a near-by river. Eventually the cave's ceiling collapses (*below*). By this time, the water has managed to eat through the underlying rock (*bottom*), starting another cave. Erosion has also deepened the river, leaving the original cave dry, except for rainwater seeping down.

river. They are known as flood plains. During seasons of high water a river may overflow its banks, adding a fine layer of silt to the entire area.

If the layers of rock a young river cuts through are of different hardness, a cross-section of the valley will look like a pair of staircases facing each other. In its Grand Canyon, the youthful river Colorado has been eroding this kind of staircase valley for 10 million years, producing the most striking landmark in the United States. In spots, the canyon is cut 6,000 feet into the Colorado Plateau. Since Lake Mead, downstream, is 2,000 feet lower than the upper canyon bed, it is clear that the Grand Canyon is destined to be dug a lot deeper in the next few million years.

When those last feet have been removed, the Colorado will no longer be a young river. Down-cutting will be at an end and the river will undertake a new project, side-cutting. Its side-to-side meanderings will mean eventual doom for every pinnacle, butte and mesa that now stand so spectacularly in the 12-mile gap between the north and south rims. Eventually, even the rims will be pushed back. Given enough time, and if there are no new upheavals in the region, the Grand Canyon of the distant future will consist of two lines of slanted bluffs with a 50-mile-wide flood plain between them. Through the plain, riding on top of a thick blanket of its own sediments, will flow a gentle, elderly river Colorado.

Stripes of Ice and Earth

Like tributary streams that join to make a river, many glaciers creep out of their valleys to create a vast ribbon of ice, Barnard Glacier in Alaska. The dark stripes are moraines, composed of dirt and rock that glaciers have collected along their edges as they ploughed along the valley floors.

Whilst streams run, glaciers merely crawl. Yet flowing ice can be one of the greatest forces of erosion. A glacier is an accumulation of snow that has slowly been compressed into ice. Eventually its weight gets so immense that it begins to flow downhill, gouging the bedrock in its path with stones and boulders embedded in its bottom, bulldozing soil and whatever else may be in the way. But a river goes as far in a few seconds as an average glacier does in a year. While some glaciers in Alaska advance as much as 40 feet in a day, many in the Alps creep downhill only a foot a day.

But it is not speed that accounts for a glacier's power. A glacier 1,000 feet thick exerts

a force of nearly 30 tons on each square foot on the valley floor underneath it, and the pressure enables the stones dragged along by the glacier to scour and polish the bedrock below. Valleys are begun by streams, but glacial erosion remodels the contours left by running water. The result is a U-shaped valley with a broad, flat floor and steep sides, strewn with rock debris deposited as the glacier recedes.

Until quite recently wind too was thought to be a major force of erosion. The weirdly balanced rocks, arches, spires, pinnacles and natural bridges of desert areas were all believed to have been shaped by the wind. Now geologists know that water was the

Pits from Rock on Rock

About 20,000 years ago, when mile-thick glaciers were moving across Canada, they gouged the underlying earth. Their tremendous pressure forced rocks frozen into the base of the ice against the ground, making ridges and grooves like these—some of which are a mile long and 200 feet deep.

principal agent, for wind must carry sand before it can cut, and even a strong wind cannot lift sand more than a few feet. Fine dust can be lifted much higher, but it is powerless to erode.

Natural arches and pinnacles often owe their shapes to mechanical weathering, a process that is noticeable in desert areas and that is helped by dry climate and wide swings in temperature. Sunlight plays a part in it: the dark-coloured mineral grains in a granite block heat up faster than the lighter ones, and their different expansion rates bring on stresses that crumble the surface. Water, freezing in rock cracks and crevices, does more. It expands by 8 per cent when it freezes, acting like a crowbar in forcing the cracks apart. Similarly, in forest areas plant and tree roots do the same thing, penetrating the soil-filled fissures and splitting the rock simply by growing.

A great deal of weathering goes on underground, too. The rain-drops that the earth soaks up fill the tiny spaces between soil and sand particles, penetrate the pores of rocks, and invade the earth's crust to a depth of hundreds of thousands of feet.

A Quiet Earth-Mover

This pretty little waterfall, spilling into a secluded pool, is actually part of nature's greatest earth-mover—the mountain stream. Heavy vegetation like that seen here helps to hold the earth in place. But the swift-running water still washes stones and soil from the uplands, carving the rock as it goes.

There is more water underground at any one time than in all the lakes and rivers combined. When the water carries enough carbonic acid—from dissolved atmospheric carbon dioxide and from decaying organic material—chemical weathering occurs. The acid eats away at the rock, and the water becomes filled with dissolved limestone in the form of a calcium carbonate solution. In limestone flats the ground may collapse, producing the pits called sink-holes.

The same percolation process has hollowed out such earth cavities as Luray Cave in Virginia, Mammoth Cave in Kentucky, and the all but endless Carlsbad Caverns of New Mexico, with their many down-growing stalactites and up-growing stalagmites, columns and solid-rock veils, all made of calcium carbonate, precipitated drop by drop.

Weathering is vital to man, for its product of crumbled rock is the chief ingredient for soil, without which man could not grow the crops he needs in order to stay alive.

The sea is also an agent of erosion. Each year, every coast line on earth is worn away by the action of the tides. Yet the ocean can add to the landscape as well as take it away. The great sand-spit called Cape Cod, for example, is being steadily devoured along its Atlantic Ocean beaches, but is being steadily rebuilt on the sheltered Cape Cod Bay side.

But the sea's prime function in the erosion cycle is to serve as a dumping ground for all the wastes of the land. The build-up of these deposits is concentrated on the continental shelves, spilling down the slope to depths of two or three thousand feet. Not much sediment from the land actually gets

A River Carves Its Course

As a river moves towards the sea, it begins to meander in a curving pattern, developing loops like those in the Yellowstone river in the American North-West, shown on the left. The water collides with the outer side of a curve, eroding the bank and picking up silt (*diagram, right*). Continuing downstream, the river drops this silt on inner curves. Thus one bank is cut away, one built up, and the river curves more sharply.

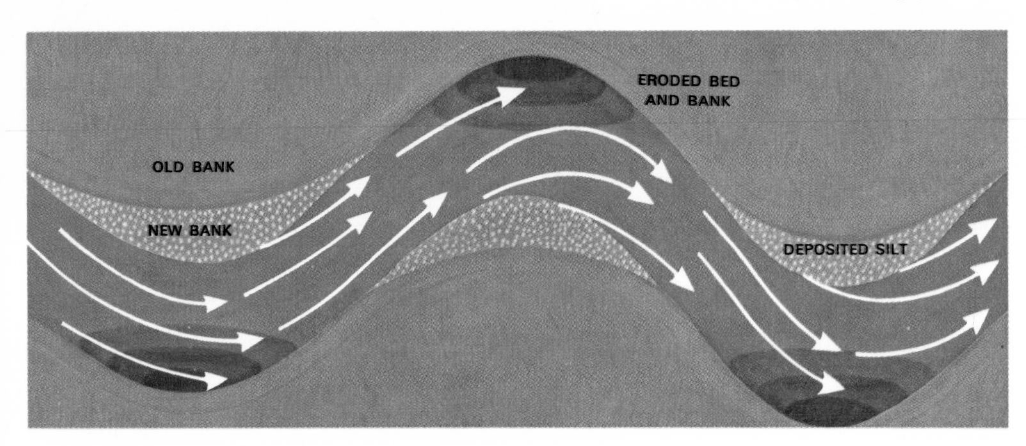

to the deepest ocean bottoms. But at river deltas, most of which are underneath the water, tremendous burdens of sediments are borne by the sea floor and the underlying crust. The Piedmont district of Italy is composed of such stream deposits, and a similar plain stretches out from the western edge of the Sierra Nevada range in the United States. Nearly every river has a delta, except where the sea is deep or turbulent. The Mississippi's mud delta is by now perhaps 30,000 feet thick and nobody knows exactly how heavy. Some geologists think that parts of the gulf floor keep sinking as more sediment piles up.

As younger sediment deposits bury older ones, the older ones are gradually compressed into solid rock by the great weight above them. Gravel beds become a rock called conglomerate, sand becomes sandstone, clayey mud becomes shale, and calcite oozes turn into limestone. Even though most sediment ends up in the ocean, the periodic upheavals of the crust along with changes of sea level during ice-ages and thaws, have succeeded in leaving sedimentary rocks almost everywhere. About 80 per cent of the earth's surface is covered by them, though by far the greater part of the crust underneath still consists of igneous rock. Each major sedimentary rock has its own rate of deposition, an arbitary measure based on the length of time it takes to build up a layer one foot thick. Although these rates can be estimated, they vary widely for each rock, depending on how favourable local conditions are. Shale, for example, may form at a rate of only one-twentieth of an inch per thousand years—

or it may build up a layer nearly two feet thick in a thousand years.

By studying these sedimentary deposits, the geologist can unravel much of the history of erosion versus diastrophism. A limestone layer, whatever its present elevation above sea level, suggests that the region once formed the bed of a sea. A seam of coal indicates an ancient swamp whose rich vegetation was partly decomposed when it was inundated by water and buried under later rock. A layer of salt or gypsum points to a body of salt water that later dried up.

Sometimes the layers are all mixed up and the history takes some deciphering. One series of sedimentary layers may lie at an angle below the surface, and another series may lie horizontally above it. This is called an unconformity, and is good evidence that three geologic processes occurred there in a definite sequence. First, beds of sediment were uplifted and left above sea level by movements of the earth's crust. Secondly, erosion worked away at the uplifted strata until they were worn flat. Thirdly, the region finally sank again below sea level, permitting more sediments to be deposited.

The Power of the Sea

These castle-like rocks off Scotland mark an older line of cliffs. The waves make such formations by attacking both sides of headlands that jut into the ocean. First they punch out enormous archways in the rock; the tops of the arches eventually crumble, leaving their foundations standing alone.

SINKING INTO THE SEA, marshes along America's Atlantic coast are disappearing at the rate of a few feet a century. About 100,000 years ago the area, called the Pamlico Terrace of South Carolina, was high and dry, dotted by low hills facing the ocean. All that is left of the hills today is a series of small islands.

5
The Ever-Moving Ground beneath Us

The solid earth underfoot is not as solid as it seems. Actually it is undergoing constant stirrings. Sometimes these take place before our eyes, as when volcanoes spurt out molten rock or earthquakes wrack the globe's thin crust. But usually the shifts are on a far slower and larger scale, as whole regions rise or subside, tilt or warp, over millions of years. In either case, no plain, no cliff is permanent. By studying the record of change written on the face of the earth, we can not only trace the geologic past but also make an educated guess at what the future holds in store.

The most striking fact about the earth's surface is that most of it—nearly three-quarters—is drowned in ocean. Still more land would be submerged if the millions of cubic miles of ice that now smother polar and mountain areas were to melt and thus raise the sea level 200 to 300 feet.

The continents of the earth are great plateaux of rock that project an average of about half a mile above the level of the sea. Ordinary maps, which divide land from sea at the shoreline, do not give a true picture of continental outlines, for they fail to show the gently sloping floor that forms the natural continuation of most coastlines. These continental "shelves", as they are called, extend out to sea in shallow water as far as 100 miles. Their total area is 10 million square miles, a little larger than North America. The steep cliffs of the continental shelves are the true limits of the continents.

The oceans also conceal the huge oceanic basins themselves. These basins average two and a third miles in depth and possess as varied a terrain as do the continents. The Mid-Atlantic Ridge, for example, is a broad submarine mountain range that runs from Iceland almost to Antarctica. Unseen by seafarers thousands of feet above, its peaks tower a mile or more above the sea floor. Mariners are familiar only with the few great mountains that thrust high enough to be visible as islands—the Azores, Ascension and Tristan de Cunha among others. Isolated peaks called sea-mounts abound in oceanic basins, and long, narrow trenches—some deeper than Mount Everest is high—scar the basin floor here and there. But for all this resemblance to the land, evidence indicates that the ocean floor is not only quite different from the continents but also has a rather different history.

An additional basic fact about the earth's crust, whether above or below water, is that it is virtually all solid rock. This is not immediately apparent, for sediments cover the ocean floor, and above water soil, vegetation, and rock fragments such as sand and gravel are littered everywhere. But this cloak is only a few feet—or perhaps yards—thick, while the thickness of the underlying bedrock is measured in miles. Furthermore, the rocks at the surface of the earth's crust are much the same as those deeper down, right to the level of the mantle. Mine and well shafts, the deepest of which descend five miles, go through the same stuff all the way down. Similarly volcanic rock shows no great differences, whether it has risen in molten form from chambers just a few miles below ground or from depths as great as 100 miles.

Rocks all belong to three great groups: the igneous, the sedimentary and the metamorphic. All igneous rocks were once molten and are believed to have come from deep in the earth, cooling at various rates and assuming various forms ranging from smooth basalt to grainy granite. Sedimentary rocks, as their name implies, are formed of layers of such materials as sand and clay washed down into lake beds and ocean floors. These sediments may be laid down by water, by ice or by wind. Cemented under pressure and often raised up again by later earth movements, they include sandstones and shales, limestones and dolomites. It is in these rocks, particularly in shales and limestones, that fossil deposits are found. The metamorphic rocks are also aptly named: they are changed in form, reborn by heat and pressure during periods of deep burial. Thus slate was once clay,

Currents in "Solid" Rock

Beneath the earth's crust is the mantle, composed of what might be called "solid" rock. But even rock can flow, and this is exactly what scientists think is happening. Warmer, lighter rock from the bottom of the mantle gradually rises, forcing the crust apart and creating volcanoes and undersea ridges. At the top of the mantle the rock cools and becomes heavier; as it sinks, it pulls the crust downwards. This forms deep faults and trenches, builds mountains, and causes the continents to move (*next page*).

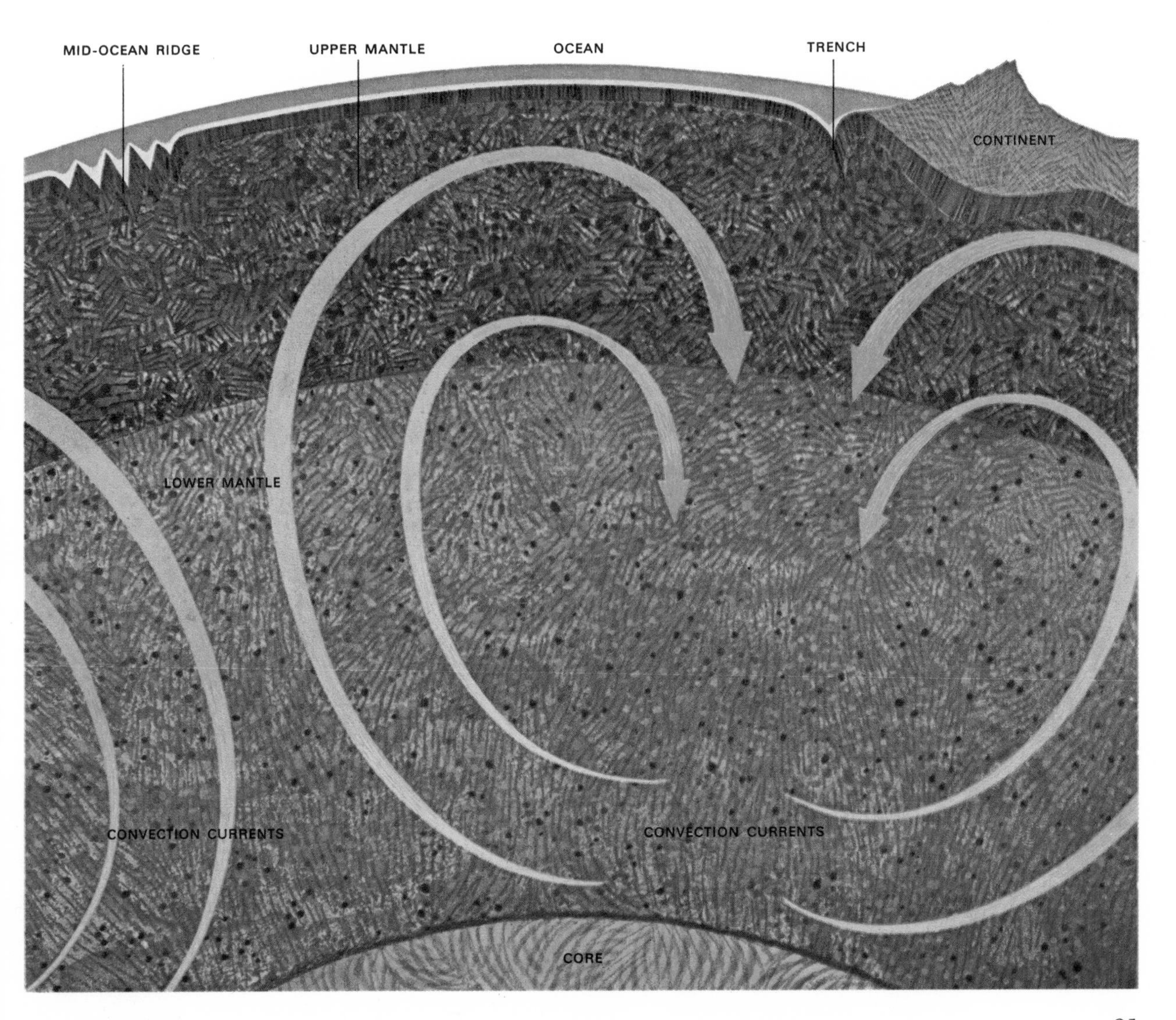

Adrift on a Sea of Rock

THE BIRTH OF THE CONTINENTS, many scientists believe, began more than 200 million years ago. Originally there was one land mass. Then it began to break up. In the illustration on the left, the continents are shown as they may have appeared then, with Europe and Asia as one mass and all the rest of the continents bunched together in the other.

THE CONTINENTS TODAY are clearly separated. Antarctica has moved hundreds of miles due south, Australia is several thousand miles to the south-east, and North and South America are separated from Africa and Europe by the Atlantic Ocean. Africa, once connected to the Americas on its west coast, is now joined to Asia by the Middle East.

CONTINENTS OF THE FUTURE may change the world map considerably in 30 million years. In this view, California, already drifting westwards from the rest of North America at the rate of two inches a year, has become an island. Florida has linked with South America. Africa has drifted away again and the South Pacific islands are joining together.

quartzite is a changed form of sandstone, and marble began as limestone.

However they have been formed, rocks are complex mixtures of various elements in the form of mineral compounds. Of the 92 natural elements known on the earth, only eight are commonly involved in rock formations; they account for 98 per cent of the earth's crust by weight. The most abundant element in the crust—47 per cent of it—is oxygen. Silicon is next, at 28 per cent. From there the percentages fall off sharply: aluminium totals 8 per cent, iron 5 per cent; and sodium, narnesium, potassium and calcium less than 4 per cent each. These eight common elements, together with several not so common ones, combine to form the nearly 2,000 known minerals. In terms of volume, oxygen-silicon compounds predominate, and only a dozen or so mineral compounds account for the bulk of the earth's crust.

Man's only direct experience with rock formation comes from what he has seen of active volcanoes—openings in the earth's crust from which molten rock pours forth. Such molten stuff is called magma when underground and lava when it emerges, and the nature of a volcanic eruption depends upon the composition of the rock and the amount of gas and water it contains. A thick, slow-flowing magma, laden with gas, tends to escape explosively, spewing fragments of solidified lava and clouds of steam and hot gases. A thinner magma, with a

A Sea-Bed in the Air

These weirdly twisted peaks in Western U.S.A. are the work of two great earth-shaping processes. Millions of years ago, when an inland sea covered the area, layers of sediment were deposited, and slowly compressed by the weight of newer layers into rock. Finally there was a gigantic upheaval, which tipped and warped the layers to form this folded mountain.

smaller gas content, pushes out in quieter fashion, forming tongues of white-hot lava that creep downhill until they harden.

The giant volcanoes that have formed the Hawaiian Islands rear as high as 30,000 feet above the ocean floor and about 14,000 feet above sea level. Lava from the active volcanoes of Hawaii often emerges as a glowing, highly fluid stream, sometimes spurting up in fountains when a pocket of gas comes to the surface. Such flows may travel for long distances before solidifying; they produce wide-based mountains. Volcanoes with thick lavas, on the other hand, build up steep, narrow cones.

Magma does not always reach the surface by the volcanic route. In fact, it sometimes does not reach the surface at all. If it can find no outlet, or if there is not enough pressure behind it to force one, it may merely thrust its way up into cracks or between layers of rock near the surface. Sometimes it forms underground lakes, pushing up the surface above like a blister but not breaking through. Often it runs along natural fissures, occasionally engulfing and melting what lies in its path. Magma that has worked its way into a vertical crack and hardened there like a wall is called a dike. Dikes vary in width from a few inches to several yards and may be many miles in length. They may be revealed millions of years after their formation when the softer rock around them has been eroded away, leaving the dikes, exposed to the elements, running like long fences across the surface of the land. A few dikes are immense. One in Rhodesia is 300 miles long and up to five miles wide.

A horizontal sheet of solidified magma is known as a sill. The magnificent cliffs known as the Palisades that line the bank of the river Hudson opposite New York City are in reality a tremendous sill. The most gigantic of all molten rock formations are batholiths, enormous bodies of granite-like rock that may be tens of thousands of square miles in area, extending downwards to unknown depths.

The texture and appearance of magma vary enormously according to whether the magma has been cooled rapidly on the surface of the earth in the form of lava or whether it has remained underground in batholiths and cooled very slowly. The rapid cooling of lava gives it a fine-grained character ranging all the way from obsidian, which is the most quickly cooled of all lava and looks like blackish glass, to basalt, a smooth, dark, dense material that is the most common of all volcanic rocks. Underground magma cools so very slowly that its structure is much coarser. Dikes and batholiths are made of granite, which is a grainy rock, speckled in colour and full of relatively large particles of different minerals.

The earth's crust appears to consist of a spherical shell of basaltic rock, in which the vast blocks of granite rock that make up the continents "float". This picture of the crust is a little oversimplified, since granite and basalt are both igneous rock, and there is a good deal of the other two basic types—sedimentary and metamorphic—on the earth's surface. However, both are much less abundant than igneous rock.

At the beginning of the 19th century, the idea that there were three basic types of rock was still a new one. Geology at that time was a highly practical, applied science concerned chiefly with the mining of commercially important deposits of metals and other minerals. Nevertheless, there were those who went beyond the pick-and-shovel stage and speculated on how the rocks got there in the first place, and why there were so many kinds. The theorists quickly found themselves in two rival groups. One group held that the earth had originally been covered with a thick sea and that everything now found in the crust—hard stones, soft stones, large and small stones, even fossils—was sediment that had been deposited by this sea. Because they took this view of the oceanic origin of the earth's crust, these men were known as Neptunists, after Neptune, the Greek god of the sea. Their opponents held that the principal factor in crust formation was the outpouring of volcanoes past and present. For their support of fire, they were known as Plutonists. Pluto, after whom they were named, was the Greek god of the underworld.

Yet these two schools were arguing over only the small portion of the earth's crust that could be inspected on the surface. The

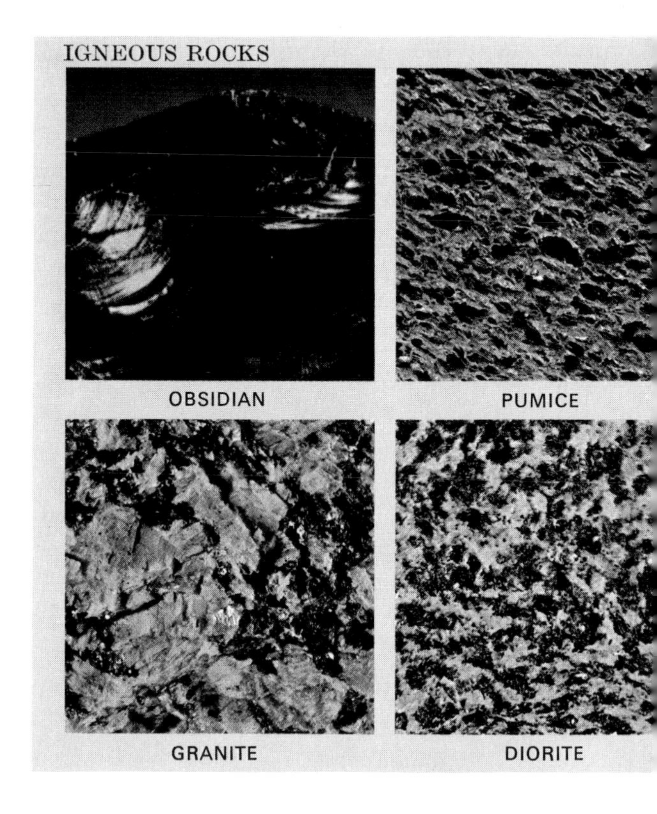

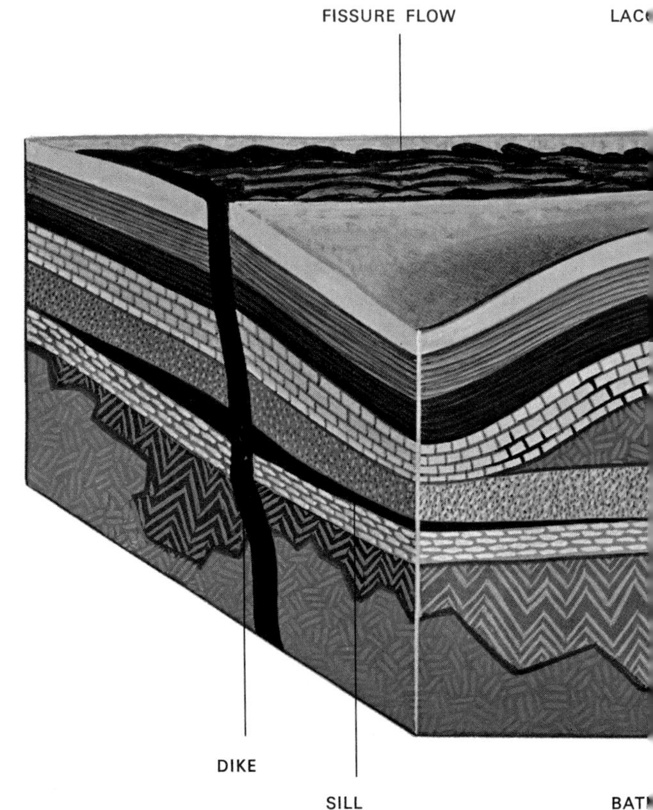

TUFF RHYOLITE

GABBRO BASALT

Rocks Formed by Heat

Igneous rock begins as magma, or molten rock, far below the earth's surface. Many kinds of igneous rock cool and harden underground; the diagram below indicates the several forms such rock may take. If it finds a pipeline to the surface, then cools and blocks the pipe, it is called a dike (*far left*). If it spreads out horizontally, it forms a sill. Batholiths occur when magma forces its way between layers of existing rock, while laccoliths force rock layers apart, and make surface rock bulge. When molten rock does reach the surface it may merely flow from an opening, forming a fissure flow or pool of rock, or a shield volcano. In a more violent volcano, molten rock and gases burst forth, spewing lighter forms of igneous rock to form a cone. The rocks at the left are some of the most common igneous rocks. The first three in the bottom row were formed underground; the rest were formed on the surface.

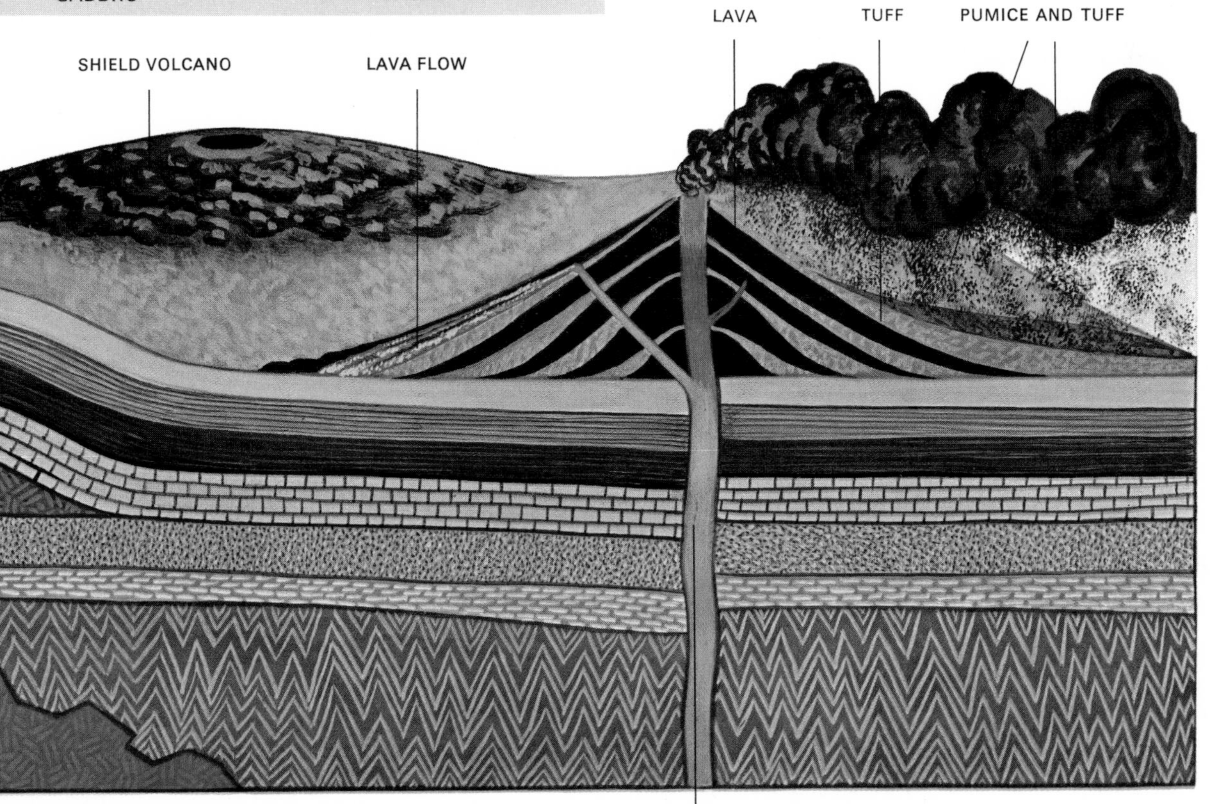

modern concept of the continents—that they are buoyant blocks of granite floating on the earth's mantle—was then unheard of. It had apparently occurred to nobody to wonder why the continents project upwards the way they do.

On a world average, the continents protrude almost three miles above the ocean floors, and probably have since the beginning. What keeps these weighty continental blocks from sinking downwards until they are level with the rest of the earth's crust? Even the most rigid shell of basalt could not withstand the constant pressure of such enormous masses of granite.

The answer to this appears to be the same as the answer to why a cork floats: in both cases, the bodies are buoyant because they are less dense than the material in which they are immersed. In the case of the continents, it is the earth's mantle that plays the part of water, supporting the colossal corks, the continents. Granite is about 20 per cent lighter than the material that makes up the earth's upper mantle. Basalt, on the other hand, is only 10 per cent lighter. The continents thus *must* ride higher above the mantle than does the crust's basaltic, basement layer.

Another problem presents itself here. A cork does not float *on* water but *in* it. How far in is determined by a simple law discovered 2,200 years ago by Archimedes: if the cork weighs a pound, it will float just deep enough to displace a pound of water. In the same way, do the great blocks of granite that compose the continents have roots substantial enough for them actually to be floating like corks? Scientific investigation indicates that the continents indeed have massive roots that reach deep down to support the three miles or so that these blocks extend above the ocean floor.

A simplified model of the crust used by many geophysicists in their calculations has a three-mile-thick layer of basalt on top of the mantle. Upon this are set the continental blocks, an average of 20 miles thick. The blocks are so heavy that they press the underlying basalt layer down about 14 miles into the mantle, thus making the mantle's surface slightly dimpled.

The idea that a continent—or any major land mass, such as a large island—floats on the mantle is illustrated by the fact that the entire Scandinavian peninsula is rising in the air. Pressed down by the weight of glaciers during the Ice Age, it has been rising ever since the glaciers departed 9,000 years ago. Scandinavia is now believed to stand nearly 1,000 feet higher than it did under the burden of the glaciers, and parts of it are now going up at the rate of three feet a century. Some estimates indicate that it still has about 650 feet to go.

Just as the roots of continental blocks thrust deep enough to dimple the underlying mantle, so the roots of mountain ranges push down even deeper in order to support their weight, and to justify their greater

Rocks Made by Pressure

As soon as a mountain is built, water and ice begin tearing it down. Water seeps into cracks, expands as it freezes, and breaks off large chunks, which form rock slumps. A glacier picks up rock and dirt, depositing them in a pile, or moraine. Mountain streams deposit sediment in an alluvial fan. The streams drop the largest rocks first, to form breccia. Smaller bits are deposited downstream and eventually turn to sandstone, while the tiniest particles of clay are carried to the end of the river and are compressed into shale. All sedimentary rocks are formed by the pressure exerted by newer layers of sediment upon the old. Swamp vegetation trapped in these layers turns to coal. Minerals from coral reefs are dissolved by the ocean, then deposited on the sea floor to become limestone.

SEDIMENTARY ROCKS

BRECCIA
CONGLOMERATE
SANDSTONE
BITUMINOUS (SOFT) COAL
SHALE
LIMESTONE
COQUINA
GYPSUM
TRAVERTINE

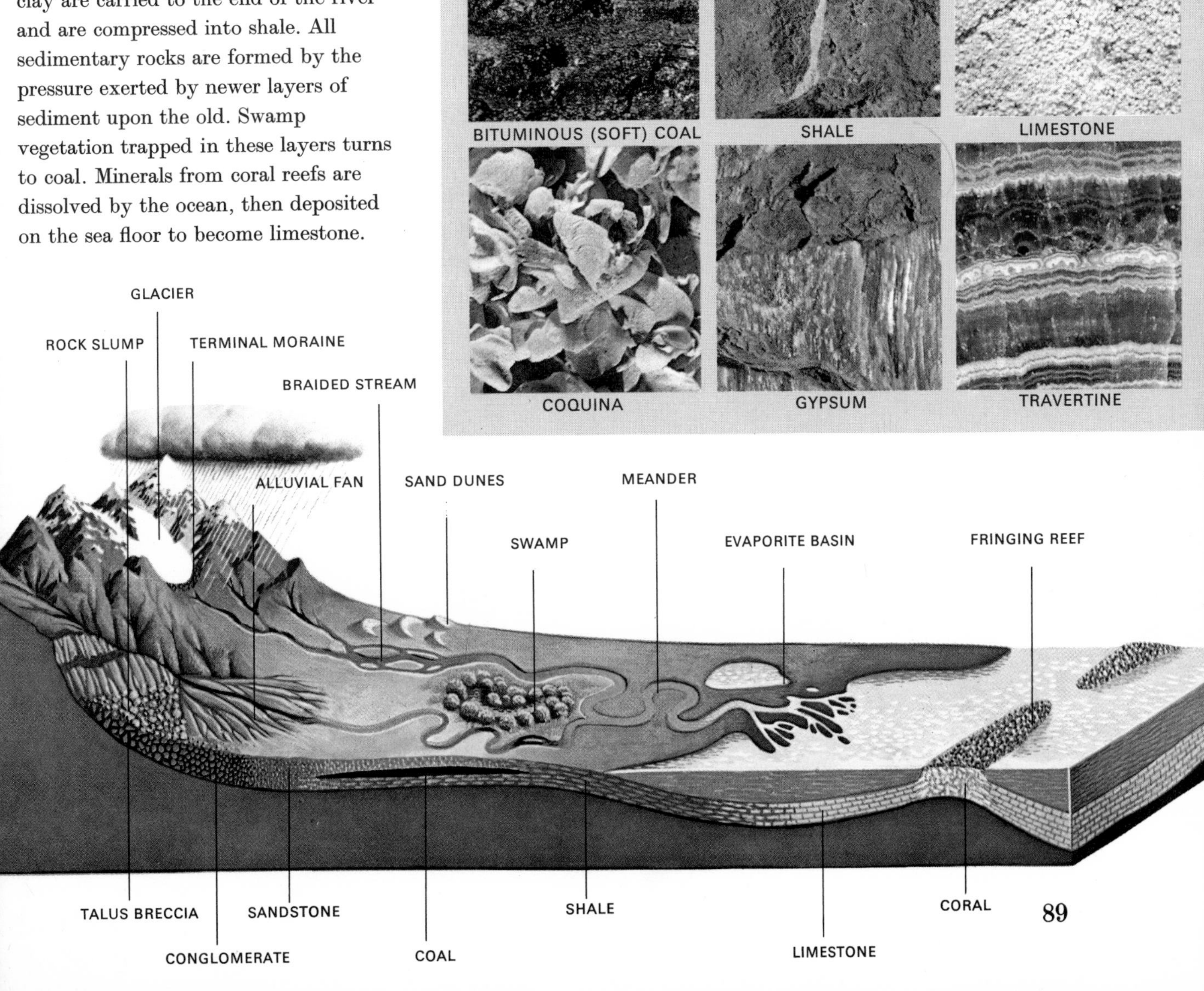

Rocks That Change

Under intense heat and pressure, sedimentary rock can be changed into the third basic type of rock, metamorphic (from the Greek for "changed"). How this happens is shown in the sectioned drawing below. At the far left, molten granite has forced its way into contact with layers of limestone, sandstone and shale. Although the heat is not enough to melt the rocks, it does alter their structure: limestone becomes marble, sandstone turns to quartzite and shale is changed to hornfels, a type of slate. At the right is shown the effect of great pressure and temperature caused by buckling in the earth's crust. Shale undergoes a succession of changes, and may end up as a form of granite. The photographs on the left include the major sedimentary rocks (limestone, sandstone and shale) and the metamorphic rocks they can become.

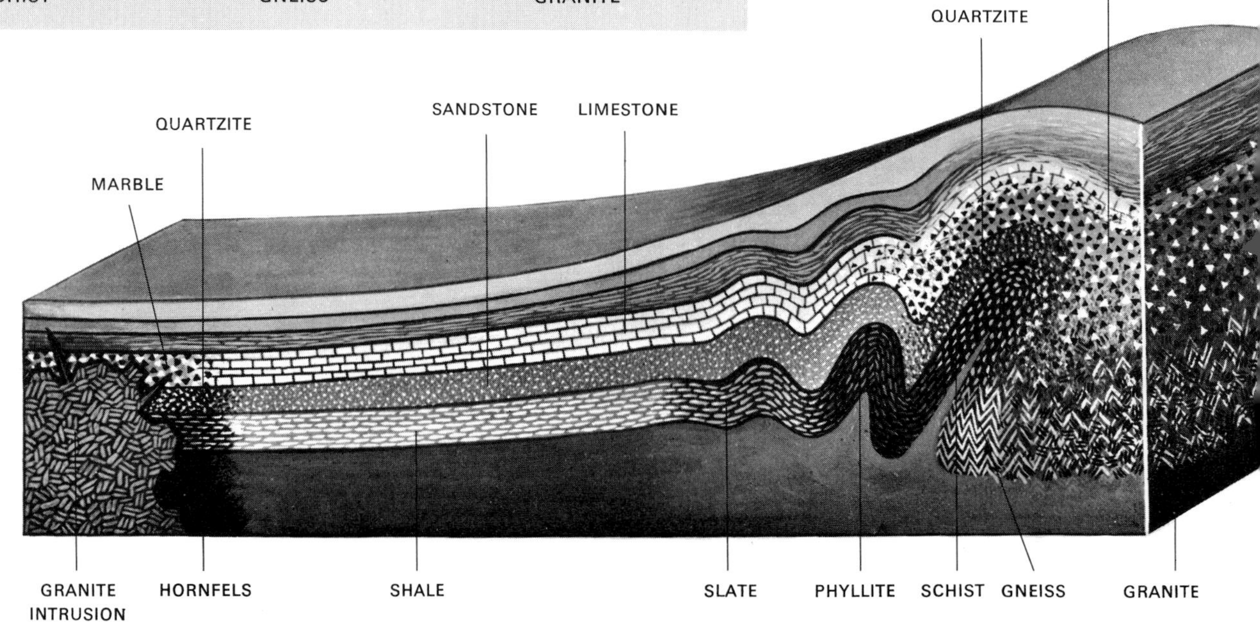

height. Mountain rock is lighter than the rock that makes up the remainder of a continent. Thus mountains "float" in the continents as the continents float in the mantle.

This theory, however, says nothing about how continents came into being. This is one of the most difficult questions that one can ask about the earth, and is the subject of intense study and controversy at this moment. There are many more suggestions than there are continents—nearly as many as there are geologists. No single theory is free from serious objections. The theory of continental drift, long dismissed by most geologists, is now becoming the most widely accepted theory that accounts for the formation of the continents. It was proposed by a German meteorologist, Alfred Wegener, who wanted to explain the parallel development of living things throughout the world. Similar plants and animals have existed in widely separated regions throughout geologic history, a fact that troubled many biologists early in this century. A common explanation was the supposed existence of land bridges linking the various continents, but this idea is hard to accept; there is no trace today of most of the supposed bridges. Wegener suggested instead that once there was a single, giant continental mass, and that the rest of the globe was covered by a single ocean. In time the huge continent cracked apart, and the pieces wandered to produce the continents of today.

This simple idea permitted Wegener to account for a number of odd facts besides the similarity in the patterns of evolution. For one thing it suggested an explanation for why South Africa, India, Australia and part of South America bear the unmistakable scars of prehistoric glaciers and ice sheets. This is understandable if it is assumed that these lands once surrounded the South Pole, which Wegener believed had been near the west coast of Africa. Similarly, the coal deposits of Europe, North America and Antarctica suggest that continents were probably situated near the equator in the past. Merely glancing at a globe seems to verify continental drift: the coastline of the Americas closely matches that of western Europe and Africa, as if the two had actually been torn apart at some time in the past. There are even matching rock formations in Norway and Canada in the north, and in South Africa and South America in the south.

Recent findings indicate that the continents may very well have shifted their positions in the remote past. These findings were made by a most ingenious method and are based on the fact that many rocks contain compounds of iron. By whatever process these rocks are formed, during the time that they are hardening the mineral grains in them will become magnetized in the direction of the earth's magnetic field, just as iron filings line up in the magnetic field of a magnet. Theoretically, if there were never any continental movement or

(Text continued on page 94)

CHALCANTHITE

GARNET

BOTRYOIDAL AZURITE, MALACHITE, LIMONITE

CHRYSOTILE (ASBESTOS)

PYRITE, QUARTZ

VARISCITE

A spectacular display, from fragile fibres to gleaming gems suggests th

YELLOW WULFENITE

AMETHYST

MICROCLINE, SMOKY QUARTZ

PEACOCK COAL

RUBY SPHALERITE

PELE'S HAIR

reat variety among the 2,000-odd minerals found in the earth's crust.

Diamonds From the Deep

Diamond, the hardest natural material, is thought to be made some 240 miles below the earth's surface, where temperatures are about 3,000°C. and pressures are over a million pounds per square inch. Diamonds are carried to the surface in volcanic eruptions, which after they have cooled leave a plug in the crust. One plug in South Africa, now mined and abandoned (*left*), produced £80 million worth of diamonds in 26 years. Below is a rough diamond found in South Africa. On the right is a pan of gem stones, which have been washed in acid. They are worth about a third of a million pounds sterling.

shifting of the poles, those grains, once hardened into position, would always point in the direction of the present magnetic poles. The fact that many such polarized rocks have their magnetic fields pointing in different directions suggests either that the poles have moved, or that the rocks themselves have.

There are good theoretical reasons for believing that the magnetic and geographic poles, while they are known to move somewhat relatively to each other, do not ever vary by more than about 10 or 12 degrees. Therefore, any polarized rocks that point farther than that from the magnetic north can be assumed to have moved—or the continents in which they lie may have moved. The evidence indeed indicates some continental drift.

One of the big problems that needed to be solved before scientists could accept this theory was that of how the continents could move in the supposedly rigid ocean floor. Now, recent evidence has shown that the ocean floors are continually moving, pushing and dragging the continents with them.

Two other theories of continental formation command more serious attention today. The older is the contraction theory, first

proposed late in the 19th century and later modified and extended into a consistent and logical—but not necessarily correct—picture. In this view the primitive earth, at some time prior to 3,000 million years ago, had a thin, uniform cover of basaltic rock. As the underlying mantle cooled, the surface shrank and began to crack, since the inner part of the earth maintained a constant temperature and volume. Through the cracks steam, gases and magma escaped, forming respectively the oceans, the atmosphere and the nuclei of the continents. Then erosion went to work. It washed rock fragments into thick beds of sediment along the margins of the small continents, and the pressure of these beds promoted further cracking just off shore. These new fractures permitted more steam, gases and magma to emerge from the earth's interior, adding to the oceans and the atmosphere and causing the growth of mountain ranges along the edges of the continents. As time went on, the continents grew larger and larger because of the new material added to their edges by the fracture system; the fractures in turn were largely brought on by the deposit of sediments made by the erosion of the continents.

This theory assumes that the crust contracted, which turns out to be rather hard to account for on the basis of pure surface cooling. Perhaps contraction was brought about by the escape of steam, gas and magma through chance fissures, and that the loss of this material led to the shrinking of what was the initial surface of the earth. Thus the original skin could have been at what is now the Mohorovičić discontinuity, and everything above it today exuded from below during thousands of millions of years.

Attention must still be paid to the convection-current theory, which argues that there are immense flows of material within the mantle, much like those that occur in a pot of porridge bubbling on a hot stove. It is believed that the action of such currents would be to concentrate the lighter granitic crustal material into large continental masses on the surface, almost like froth. This theory must assume that both granite and basalt were part of the primeval pre-continental crust, but there is nothing to indicate that this was not so. It must also deal with the fact that the flow of material in the mantle is not a flow at all in the sense that we normally understand it, but is incredibly slow, perhaps about an inch a year. However, we are dealing with immense periods of time, and the important thing is to establish some movement, however small. An inch a year, over millions of years, amounts to hundreds of miles.

Both of these recent theories have their strong points. Many geologists today lean towards a combination of the two, with contraction playing the larger role and convection currents a lesser one.

While these two theories are currently receiving the most attention from geophysicists, new ones are constantly being suggested. It has been proposed by the marine geologist Bruce Heezen that the earth is expanding. Only in this way can he account for much that still remains obscure in the history of the earth. Expansion would crack the crust along fracture lines through which new material would well up, and as the sections of the crust moved apart, immense pressures would be exerted upon the contents to squeeze mountains upwards. This is a novel and, at first glance, startling idea —but at the present stage of its development it is an idea to be further explored.

Prospecting for Uranium

Using a Geiger counter, a prospector searches over a vein of yellow carnotite. This material, found mostly in the Colorado Plateau, is a major source of uranium in the United States. When the metal is purified, it becomes the fuel for nuclear reactors, as well as the basic ingredient for nuclear bombs.

6

A Record of Life in the Rocks

DRILLING FOR BONES, workmen clear rock away from a dinosaur skeleton at the Dinosaur National Monument in Utah in the American west. The bulk of the rock is broken away with the drill, and the bones are freed with delicate tools. Discovering such bones tells us much about animals that lived before man existed.

How old is the earth? One way of measuring its age is to determine the age of the rocks of the earth's crust, many of which have existed for millions and millions of years. The study of ancient layers of rock has told scientists many things, not only about age, but about evolution and the conditions of climate that existed in the distant past.

The measuring stick that is used is radioactive dating. A radioactive element is useful because it has a precise rate of decay. Atom by atom, it turns into a more stable element. Radioactive carbon, known as carbon-14, loses exactly half its store of radioactivity in 5,730 years by conversion into nitrogen. A specialist with delicate measuring instruments can compare the amount of radioactive carbon remaining in a fossil with the amount of ordinary carbon, and in that way calculate how old the fossil is. For in the first 5,730 years the amount of radioactive carbon will drop by one half and in the next 5,730 years by another half, and so on until none remains.

Radioactive carbon is a superb tool for the prehistorian. But it is less useful for the geologist, who is concerned for the most

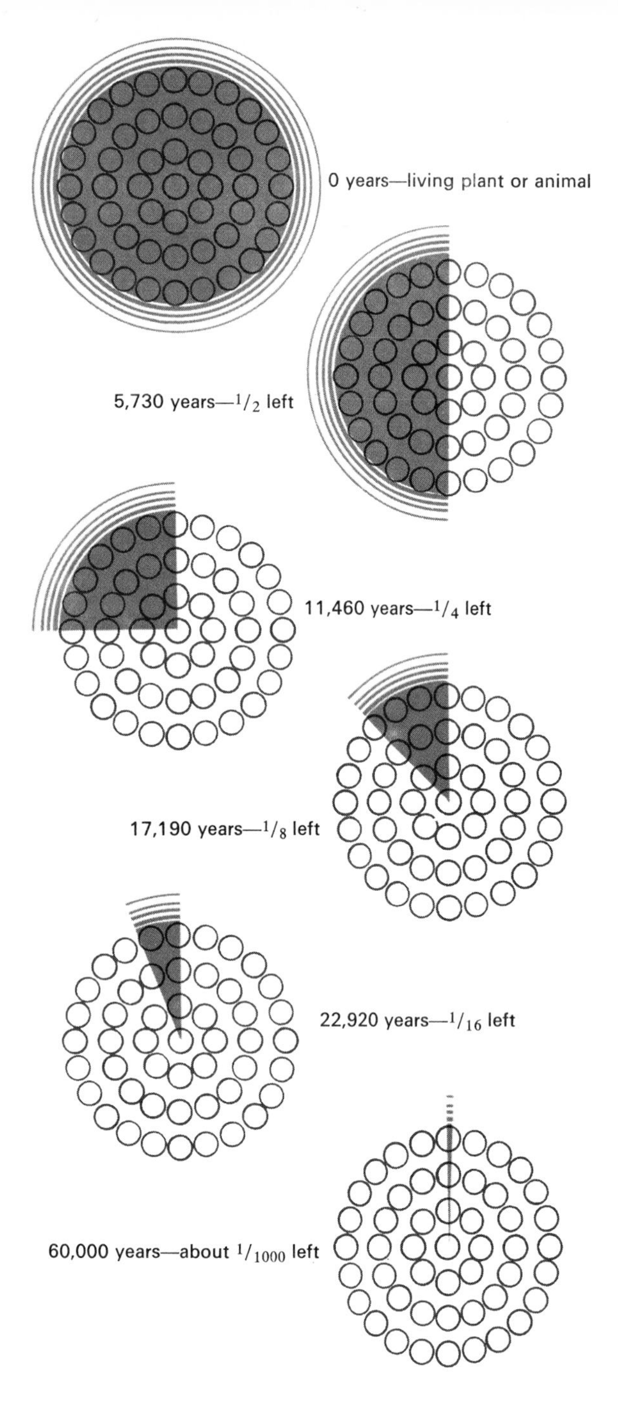

A Way of Measuring Age

These diagrams illustrate what is called the "carbon-14" method of telling a fossil's age. The tissues formed by living organisms have radioactive carbon-14 as one of their basic components. Over long periods of time, this carbon-14 decays into nitrogen. Half decays every 5,730 years, as shown above. By measuring the amount of carbon-14 that is left in a fossil the scientist can calculate its age.

part with periods of time vastly longer than its rather short half-life. He must find radioactive materials with half-lives of millions or thousands of millions of years. Luckily, they exist. An isotope of potassium decays into argon with a half-life of 1,300 million years; an isotope of thorium decays into lead with a half-life of 14,000 million years, and an isotope of rubidium decays into strontium with a half-life of 60,000 million years.

A particularly useful radioactive tool for geologists is uranium. Traces of uranium are found in many rocks and in widely scattered areas on the earth's surface. All uranium on earth will eventually become lead. However, this takes place with fantastic slowness. At the end of 4,500 million years, one-half of an original chunk of an isotope of uranium will still be uranium, and one half will have turned to lead.

The oldest known rocks today are found near Dodoma, Tanzania, in Africa. This ancient granite is approximately 3,400 million years old. The 3,400-million-year figure leaves open the question of how much older the earth is than its oldest rocks. However, the principle of radioactive dating can be applied to this problem in a most ingenious way. Recently such studies have been made of the fragments of meteorites, giving age estimates of 4,500 million years. Meteors are, like the earth, part of the solar system. Since it is generally assumed that the whole of the solar system came into existence at the same time, most geologists believe that the earth is the same age as the meteorites.

We toss millions and thousands of millions about very glibly. Yet they are such staggeringly large units of time that it is worth pausing to try to emphasize just how long 4,500 million years really is. Hendrik Van Loon did it with this fanciful opening to his famous book, *The Story of Mankind:*

"High up in the North in the land called Svithjod, there stands a rock. It is a hundred miles high and a hundred miles wide. Once every thousand years a little bird comes to this rock to sharpen its beak.

"When the rock has thus been worn away, then a single day of eternity will have gone by."

A less dramatic but perhaps more useful way of emphasizing the age of the earth is to compare it with the evolution of man. It is generally believed that human beings have evolved during the last two million years. The earth on which they evolved is more than 2,000 times that old.

What is known about the slow process that first brought life into existence on the earth? So far, almost nothing. Biochemists and physicists believe that the earth's early atmosphere and oceans contained the raw materials for the formation of protein molecules. Recent studies have indicated that the chemical broth in the ancient oceans could have been organized into amino acids through the action of lightning. Amino acids have been turned into protein molecules in the laboratory; from this all else could follow. The major requirement is time. It is

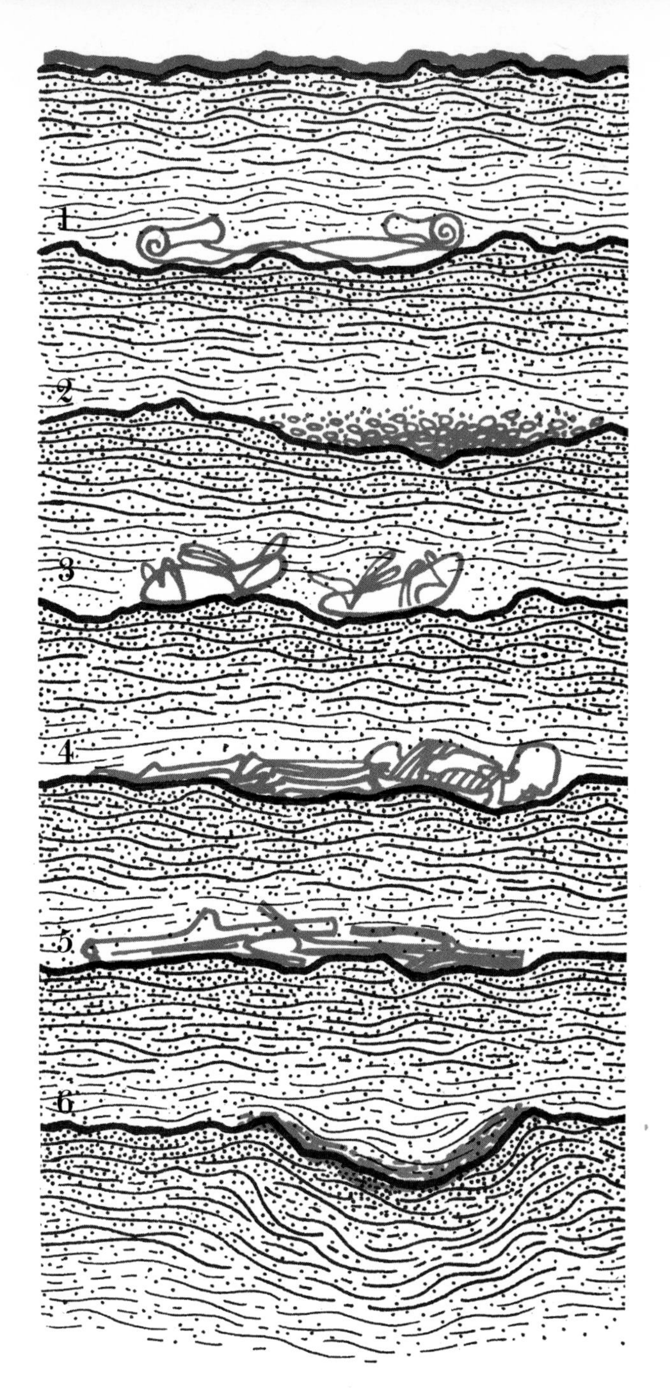

Some Fossil Treasures

Objects dated by the carbon-14 method are shown above. It proved the famous Dead Sea Scrolls *(1)* to be at least 1,900 years old. Some Japanese lotus seeds *(2)* were found to be 3,000 years old. Sandals *(3)* in an Oregon cave were dated at 9,000 years, objects near a skeleton in Illinois *(4)* at 10,000 years. A Wisconsin tree *(5)* died 11,000 years ago. Charcoal found in Iraq *(6)* kept men warm in 30,000 B.C.

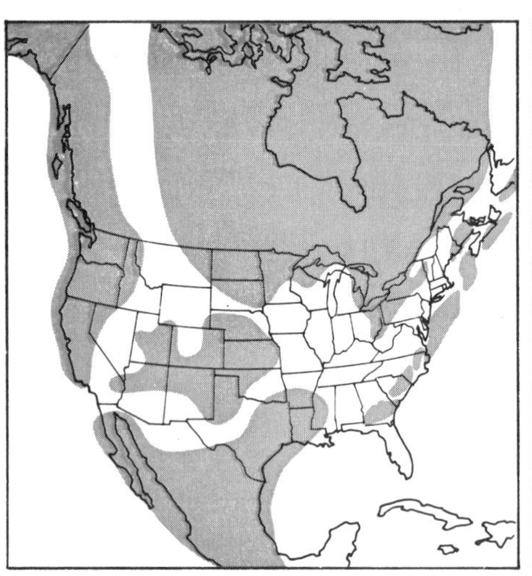

CAMBRIAN PERIOD

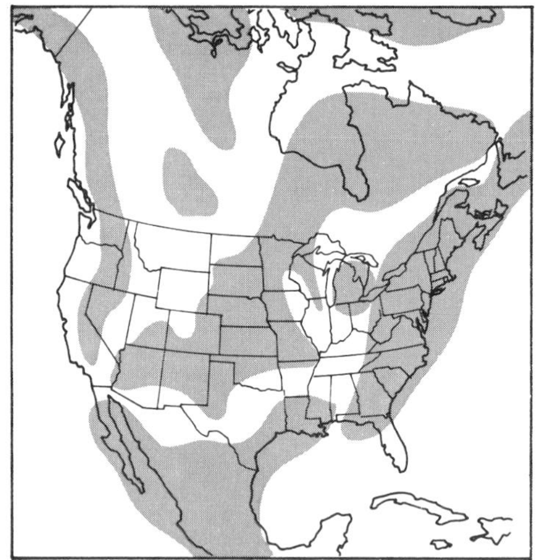

ORDOVICIAN PERIOD

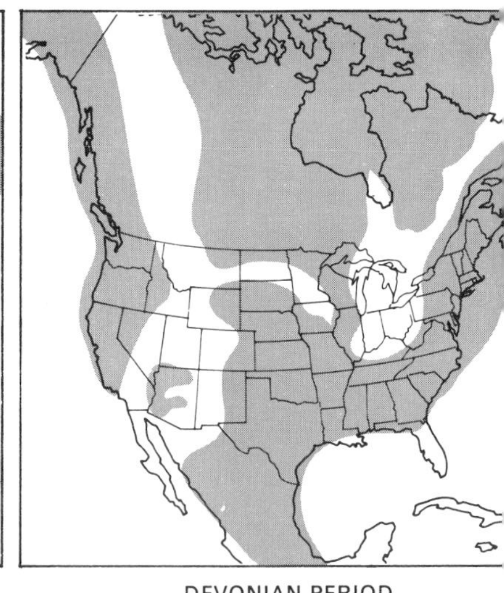

DEVONIAN PERIOD

Where the Sea Used to Be

At various times long ago, North America was covered by the sea. In the Cambrian period the sea (white) reached over much of the United States. In the Ordovician period the sea was even more extensive. By the late Devonian the land had made gains. The sea kept retreating, though in Carboniferous times most of the West was an ocean and in the Cretaceous period water reached into Canada. Not until the Miocene did the present continent almost entirely emerge.

CARBONIFEROUS PERIOD

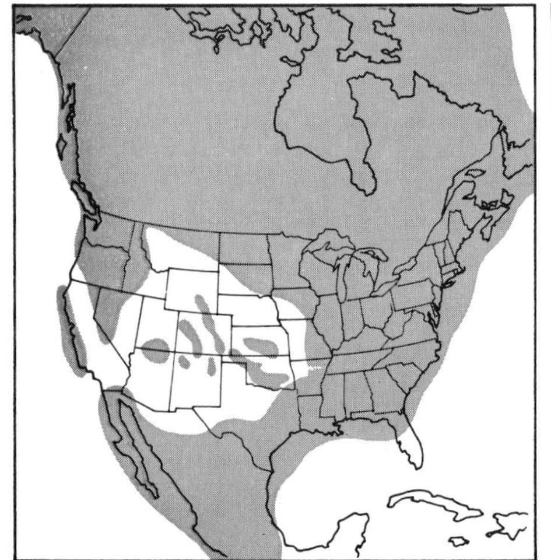

CRETACEOUS PERIOD

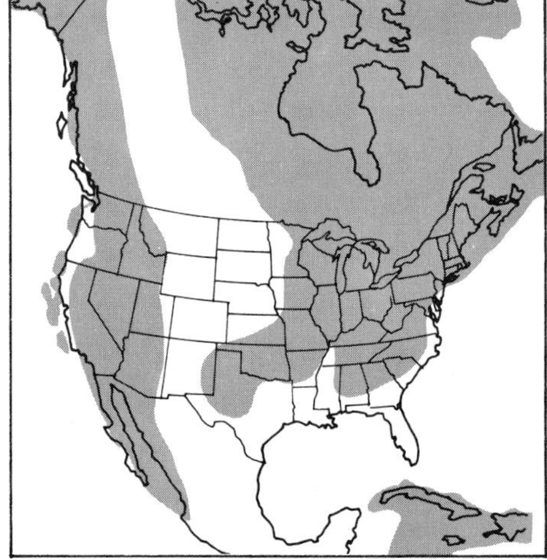

MIOCENE PERIOD

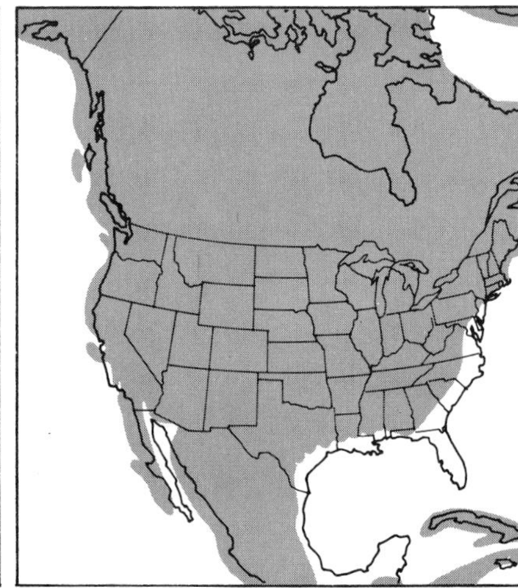

estimated that the change from simple organic compounds to the earliest one-celled organism may well have taken one-third as long as the later development from one-celled animal to man. The fossil record shows not only that time was available, but that life did get under way very slowly.

Geologists divide earth history into two periods, called aeons. The first, and by far the larger one is known as the Cryptozoic aeon, from the Greek for "hidden life". It covers the time from the earliest known rocks up to some 600 million years ago, a span of about 3,000 million years. The second, or Phanerozoic aeon—from the Greek for "visible life"—extends to today.

Rocks from the Cryptozoic aeon occur where the cores of ancient mountain systems have been laid bare by erosion or where deep gorges have been cut into high plateaux or, most important, in the form of huge exposed "shields" in a few spots on the earth's surface. These ancient outcrops constitute an enormous amount of material. And yet the only fossils so far discovered in them are a few kinds of algae and some colonies of fungus, plus the burrows of an unknown, worm-like animal. No trace of the worm itself remains.

This seems a pitifully small harvest from a 3,000-million-year segment of earth history. However, it may not be the entire story. Cryptozoan animals were all water dwellers, and probably developed few if any hard parts such as shell, cartilage or bone. There may have been many more of them, and a greater variety, than the Cryptozoan rocks show. Some Cryptozoan rocks are rich in organic carbon, and this could represent the last traces of living things. None the less, there is a startling contrast between life on earth even at the end of the Cryptozoic aeon and life in the earliest Phanerozoic.

There are three great subdivisions of the Phanerozoic aeon, known as eras. First comes the Palaeozoic era (ancient life), then the Mesozoic era (in-between life), and finally the Coenozoic era (recent life). The Palaeozoic era, which lasted 370 million years, drew to a close 230 million years ago. The Mesozoic lasted for 167 million years. The Coenozoic, the era in which we live, began only 63 million years ago.

Just as aeons are broken up into eras, so eras are divided into periods. The earth at the start of the Palaeozoic's first period, the Cambrian, was somewhat different from what it is today. The sea was probably larger than it is now. The continents were slightly lower and smaller than they are today. The rocks were bare of plant life except for lichens and a handful of other very primitive plants. There were no animals on land at all. The general atmosphere was one of mildness and calm—and apparent agelessness, for the Cambrian period went on and on in this manner for 100 million years.

In the sea, however, things were much livelier. The progression from simple organic compounds to single-celled organisms, and from there to multicelled forms, had now reached the point where the sea was swarming with a variety of creatures, some of them weighing as much as 10 pounds.

The outstanding living form of the Cambrian period was the trilobite. It was the great evolutionary triumph of its time, the most efficient thing the world had ever seen. It was a sort of cross between a lobster and a sea slug, with a lobster-like shell and numerous spindly legs. Its segmented body also allowed it to roll up into a tight ball for defence. Trilobites developed a wide variety of shapes and sizes, and were much more advanced than anything else of their day. And their day was a long one; it lasted more than 300 million years.

The Cambrian period was followed by the Ordovician. The change was marked by considerable geologic disturbance in the Western Hemisphere. For a time the oceans divided North America into a group of islands. In the seas trilobites continued in enormous throngs, but they were threatened by the emergence of cousins of the modern squid. The Ordovician also saw the appearance of the first animal with a backbone. It was only a primitive, jawless fish, but it *did* have a backbone, and is the oldest of its kind that has been found.

The following period, the Silurian, lasted a mere 20 million years. During the Silurian the eastern United States was slowly transformed by coastal uplift into a land-locked inland sea, which gradually evaporated, leaving an immense salt desert. These salt

A History of Life on Earth

The length of time that life has been evolving is shown here in two different ways. Below, the time since the earth began, 4,500 million years, is represented by a spiral measuring tape. Life began about a quarter of the way up the tape, and man developed only near the very top. On the right is a diagram of America's Grand Canyon and the animal fossils that have been found there. Here evolution's history is beautifully laid out. The river Colorado has cut through layer after layer of sedimentary rock, exposing fossils of many different periods. In the bottom layer, fossils of algae (tiny sea plants) have been found. They may be among the earliest types of life. Higher layers contain more complex forms of life. Scorpion and starfish remains, for instance, are common in the layer deposited in Cambrian times. At the top of the canyon, in layers deposited in Permian times, are more modern trees and insects.

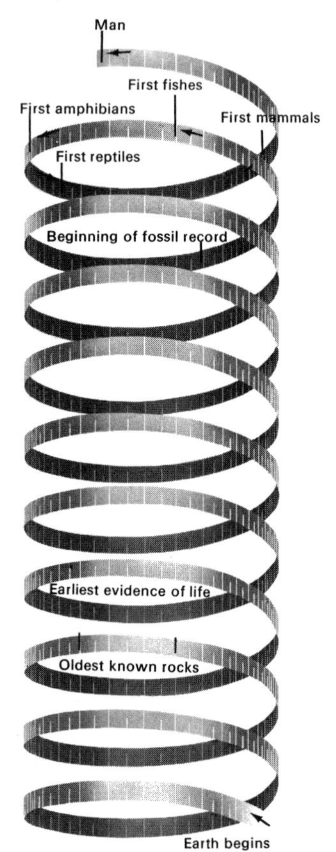

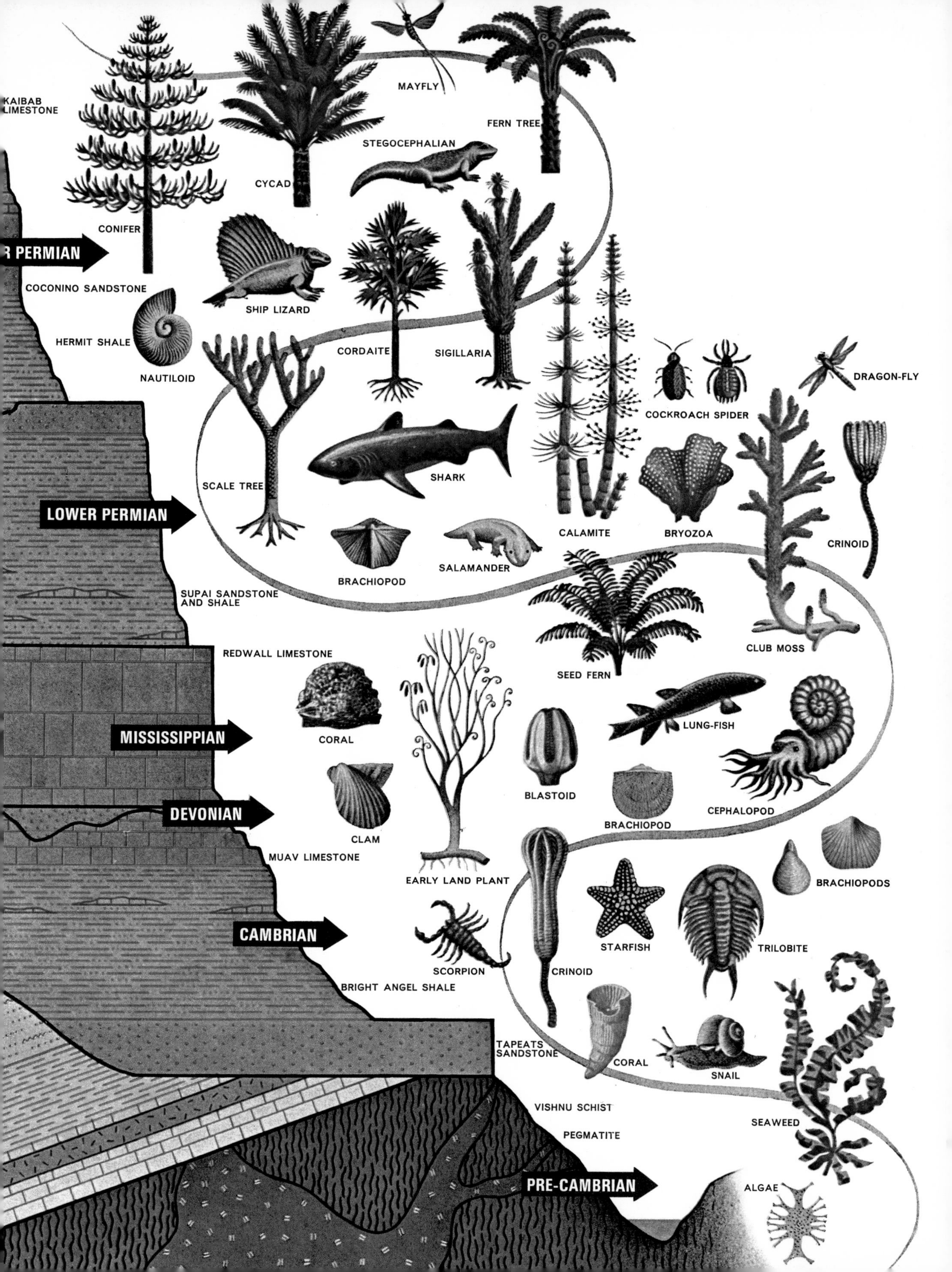
KAIBAB LIMESTONE
R PERMIAN
COCONINO SANDSTONE
HERMIT SHALE
LOWER PERMIAN
SUPAI SANDSTONE AND SHALE
REDWALL LIMESTONE
MISSISSIPPIAN
DEVONIAN
MUAV LIMESTONE
CAMBRIAN
BRIGHT ANGEL SHALE
TAPEATS SANDSTONE
VISHNU SCHIST
PEGMATITE
PRE-CAMBRIAN
CONIFER
CYCAD
MAYFLY
FERN TREE
STEGOCEPHALIAN
SHIP LIZARD
NAUTILOID
CORDAITE
SIGILLARIA
SCALE TREE
SHARK
CALAMITE
COCKROACH SPIDER
DRAGON-FLY
BRYOZOA
CRINOID
BRACHIOPOD
SALAMANDER
CLUB MOSS
SEED FERN
CORAL
LUNG-FISH
BLASTOID
CLAM
BRACHIOPOD
CEPHALOPOD
EARLY LAND PLANT
BRACHIOPODS
STARFISH
TRILOBITE
SCORPION
CRINOID
CORAL
SNAIL
SEAWEED
ALGAE

deposits have been extensively mined in New York, Pennsylvania and Michigan. Altogether, the dry salt lake may have extended over 100,000 square miles.

Life in the warm oceans continued to increase in numbers. The durable trilobite lingered on, but in modified form. Many now were covered with spines, presumably as a protection against the superior mobility of the evolving fish. Corals were very common. A gigantic water scorpion appeared, its nine-foot length an all-time record for its kind. This huge scorpion completely overshadowed a little-known relative, which was only about two inches long, but which was to be infinitely more important to the over-all course of evolution. For this small creature, along with an equally inconspicuous millepede, shares the honour of being the first animal to venture on dry land.

In the next age, the Devonian age, spiders, the first known land-dwelling animals, appeared. Fish continued to develop, but the most important one was a fish that was destined to become the ancestor of frogs and salamanders. This fish, named Crossopterygii, had a primitive set of lungs and strong, stumpy fins, which it employed to breathe air and "walk" on land.

Land plants began to develop and continued during the next period, the Carboniferous, which began 345 million years ago and lasted about 65 million years. It was a time when many mountain ranges rose and volcanoes were extremely active.

The Remains of Ancient Life

Ancient animals and plants are sometimes preserved in the form of fossils like those shown here. When a plant or animal dies it usually decays, but if it falls into a soft material such as clay, which later hardens, it may leave a perfect print (*right*). Sometimes a whole leaf can be preserved, when minerals enter the cells and harden there, as they did in the leaf at the top right. With animals, usually only the bones are preserved, as in the case of the tree climbing Uintacyon (*centre right*). A fly's entire skeleton, preserved in amber, is shown below.

PLATANUS LEAF

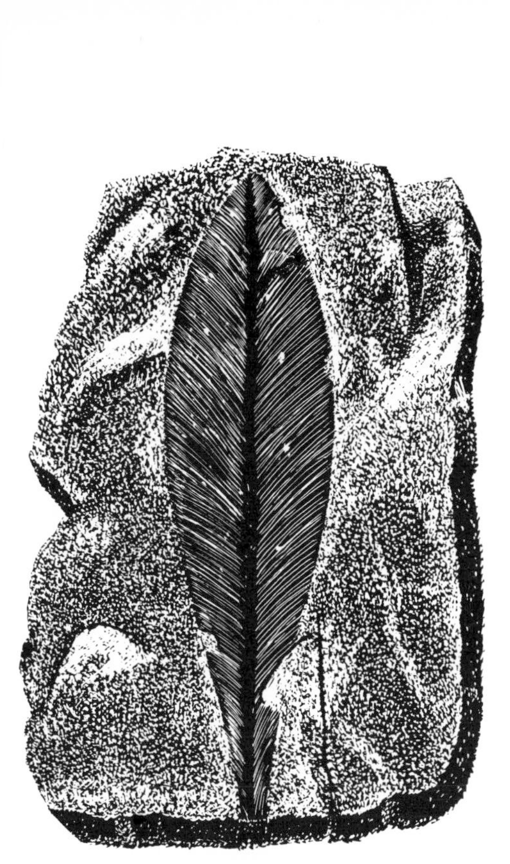

FERN LEAF

UINTACYON

FLY

On land there were vast forest swamps choked with plants and trees. These were buried in water over and over again across huge expanses of the earth's surface. Bedded down in mud, crushed by pressures from the sediments piling up above them, these forgotten forests were compressed into some of the world's great coal deposits, which give the Carboniferous period its name.

Many insects developed during the Carboniferous, including one that resembled a dragon-fly but had a two-and-a-half-foot wing spread. With them came the first traces of a new vertebrate group, the reptiles. These were the first backboned animals to free themselves completely from the water. Amphibians must return to water to mate and lay their fragile eggs; their young, just as the tadpoles of frogs still do, must pass through a free-swimming aquatic state before they can return to land in mature form. The great innovation supplied by the reptiles was that their eggs had tough cases and could be deposited anywhere without being in danger of drying up, and their young could start living on land the moment they were hatched. This final liberation from the sea ranks as a major event in the history of life.

The last of the Palaeozoic periods, the Permian, was one of the most violent in earth history. Mountain-building increased in intensity, and for the first time for hundreds of millions of years there was a drastic change in the climate. The Permian experienced severe ice-ages, which covered parts of Africa, Australia and South America with glaciers. Other parts of the world turned to deserts. Drying seas produced the three largest salt deposits in the world, one in Russia, one in Germany and one stretching from Kansas to New Mexico in the United States. Altogether, this was a very difficult period for life. The denizens of the Carboniferous swamps, both plant and animal, were ill fitted to withstand the cold and extreme dryness. Many died off. Reptiles adapted well, but in the sea the trilobite finally reached the end of the line. At last it became extinct.

Thus ended the Palaeozoic. The period that followed, the Mesozoic, lasted 167 million years. During the Mesozoic, reptiles became the dominant type of animal and, as the period wore on, they grew in both number and size. Some returned to the sea in the form of dolphin-like animals with long, toothed snouts. Others wallowed in the swamps munching enormous quantities of marsh and river plants. By the middle of the period they had evolved into the largest land animals the world has ever known.

This was the age of dinosaurs. There was the diplodocus, a "typical" dinosaur with a long neck, a tiny head containing an even tinier brain, a fat body, huge legs and a long tail. The diplodocus was 85 feet long. Tank-like animals called stegosaurs lumbered through the woods, their backs protected by huge, bony plates set on edge,

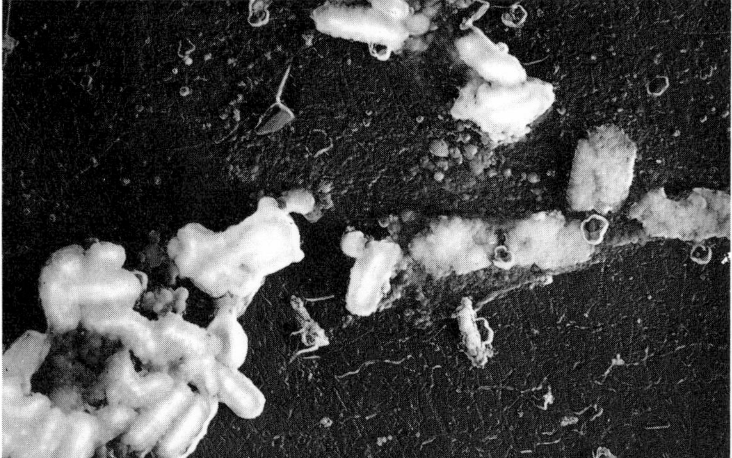

Life's Beginnings

Life on earth probably began in very simple form. Dr. Stanley Miller (*centre picture*) an American chemist, has conducted experiments showing how certain chemicals basic to living organisms could have formed when the earth was young. Although we have no record of this occurrence, we do have fossils of very ancient and very simple forms of life. The top picture shows a fossil one-celled bacterium 3,000 million years old; at the bottom is a fossil of a rod-shaped bacterium 2,000 million years old.

and their tails armed with three-foot spikes. They were slow-moving and even slower-witted creatures, with two-and-a-half-ounce brains housed in a 10-ton body.

Another group of dinosaurs were meat eaters. Agile and hungry, they ran along on their hind legs, dangling small forelegs as they went. Some were no larger than chickens. Others, like the allosaurus and the tyrannosaurus, were undoubtedly the most fearsome animals ever known, and preyed on the huge, inoffensive plant eaters. Still others took to the air, gliding over the sea on leathery wings with a spread of 25 feet. These were not birds, nor were they bats. They were flying reptiles with small bodies and thin hollow bones.

Although the Mesozoic period was dominated by reptiles, the first birds appeared then, as did the first mammals. Birds and mammals are both warm-blooded, which gives them an immense advantage over insects, amphibians and reptiles.

All cold-blooded animals, if it gets too hot, suffer heat prostration. A small lizard living in burning desert sands must scamper quickly from one patch of shade to another, or it will die in a few minutes. It is only the bird or mammal, gasping or sweating to cool its body, that can stay out in the hot sun for long periods of time. Similarly, when the temperature falls, cold-blooded animals become motionless.

Mammals, with fur and a layer of fat just beneath the skin to help to retain body heat and the ability to produce their own body heat, can stand extremes of cold almost indefinitely. On the other hand, they require a steady supply of food in order to keep their internal furnaces stoked; the extreme example is the shrew, which must eat heartily every hour or two, or it will starve to death. By contrast, a cold-blooded python needs a good meal only about once a year. During the Coenozoic era, warm-blooded animals have become dominant.

Man has now evolved to the point where he can reason, remember, read and write, devise scientific instruments and laboratories. Out of all this comes the momentous discovery that there is such a thing as evolution. Out of that comes the science of genetics—and with it the key to the shaping of the further course of evolution.

A Rare Fossil Find

A beautifully preserved fossil, this fish is called *Mene rhombeus*, and it is a relative of the modern pompano. Fifty million years ago it swam in the seas off Italy. Such fossils are extremely valuable to palaeontologists, for it is rare to find one like this in which every bone and fin is still easy to see.

7

The Uncertain Future of the Earth

No oracle of ancient times ever performed such impressive predictions as today's scientist does when he foretells the swaying of an unbuilt skyscraper in a hurricane, the spiralling orbits of an unlaunched astronaut or the power of an unexploded nuclear bomb. Yet these feats are child's play compared with the attempts of modern earth theorists to forecast the trends taking place in the land, sea and air of man's planet. Scientists hope and expect that their crystal balls will not always be so cloudy. Meteorologists, armed with computers, are already calculating day-to-day weather on the basis of mathematical models of the entire atmosphere. They are increasingly able to improve their results as they learn to use the information from orbiting weather satellites. Eventually they hope to understand long-term climates as well as short-term weather—to look months, years and perhaps even centuries into the future and predict world-wide changes in temperature, ocean level and movements of glaciers. If they are successful and can learn to forecast floods and famines well ahead of time, it will permit nations to forearm themselves

A FROZEN EARTH, pictured about 50,000 million years from now, may support no life. The moon will have drawn closer to the earth and the sun will be only a flicker. In this cold world man will have been extinct for a long time—unless he has found a way to move the human race to another planet.

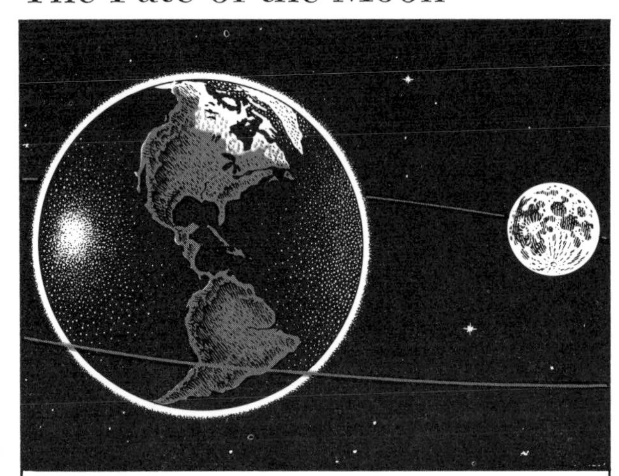

THE MOON'S POSSIBLE FUTURE is shown in these drawings. Above, the moon is seen in its present orbit, one that grows larger as the earth, spinning more slowly, exerts less pull on it.

SPIRALLING INTO SPACE, the moon continues to increase the size of its orbit as the earth's rotation continues to slow. Eventually one day on earth will be as long as a month is today.

against natural disasters and perhaps even to participate in international weather-control programmes.

Since weather is vitally important to trade and commerce, it has been studied more intensively than most earth processes. But a small, hard-working group of earth scientists is also busy measuring and analysing the other forces of change that mould the earth's future. Hardly a month goes by in which some scientist somewhere does not find evidence with which to improve or refine the explanation of some earthly phenomenon. Sir Isaac Newton explained the oceans' tides; today's physicists have added tides raised in the atmosphere by both moon and sun, and even land tides two or three inches high, raised in the solid rock of the earth's crust. To the earth's simple rotation they have added half a dozen wobbles. To visible sunlight and starlight they have added a whole spectrum of cosmic energy: radio waves, infra-red waves, ultraviolet waves, X-rays and gamma rays, and even tiny bits of matter that come cannonballing from stars that exploded long ago in the depths of space.

It may take decades to fit together all the puzzling pieces of evidence into a true portrait of the dynamic earth. No field of science encompasses such a wealth of unexplained facts. The ocean levels in the Northern Hemisphere drop eight inches every spring without any compensating rise south of the equator. No one knows where the water goes. Until as recently as 1948 the local curvature of the earth in Europe was

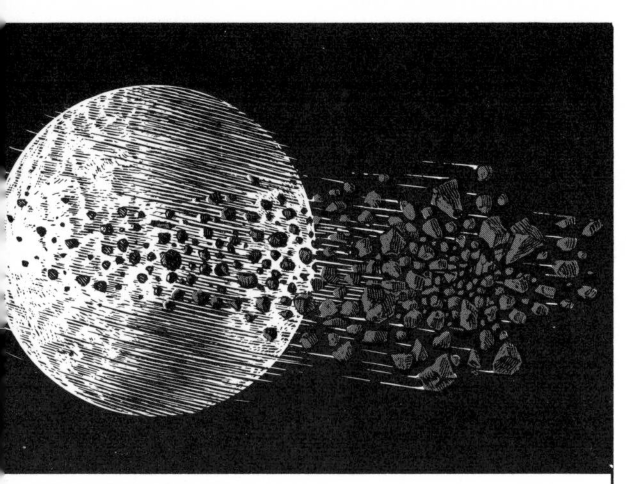

RETURNING TO EARTH, the moon responds to the earth's pull again when the earth day becomes longer than a month. If it comes too close, the earth's gravitational pull may shatter it.

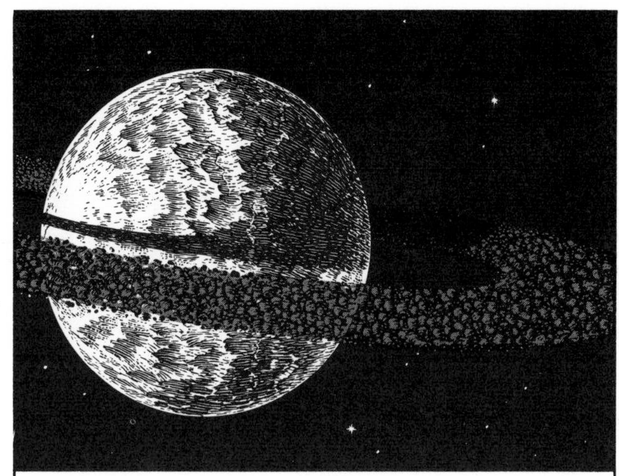

A RING AROUND THE EARTH will be formed if the satellite does break up. Observed from deep in space, the earth would then resemble the solar system's other ringed planet, Saturn.

so little known that the maps of different countries did not join properly. Maps made in Sweden differed from maps made in Denmark by 300 feet. English and French maps were out of mesh by 600 feet.

One of the most exciting discoveries in recent years is one concerning the movements of the continents. The theory that the continents "drift" around the surface of the earth is not a new one. But until recently most scientists dismissed the idea, for they could not imagine any force that would cause the drift. For a long time there had been evidence that North and South America, for example, were once connected to Europe and Africa. Just by looking at a world map, you can see how well the coastlines of these continents would fit if pushed together, almost like pieces of a jigsaw puzzle. Even more convincing evidence has been unearthed by geologists examining rock formations. Rocks of identical age and type have been found in exactly the places the continents would have meshed—on the east coast of South America and the west coast of Africa, for instance.

Now, in addition to evidence such as this, the force that could cause continents to drift has been discovered. It all began when scientists who were examining the ocean floor became puzzled at the relative newness of the sediments they found. Nowhere could they find material older than 100 million years. What was happening to older sediments? Certainly the oceans were more than 100 million years old.

Finally it was determined that the mantle

of the earth, just beneath the crust, acts like a huge endless belt (*see illustrations, page* 81). Plastic rock—rock that is hot enough to flow slowly but not actually in a molten state—rises from the earth's interior. This rising occurs along the oceanic ridges, or undersea mountain ranges. The plastic rock then travels beneath the ocean floor and descends deep into the mantle again when it reaches undersea trenches. The cause of this movement is the heat of the earth's interior. After the hot rock rises to the surface of the mantle, it is pushed along by the pressure of still more hot rock trying to reach the surface. Then as the rock cools it descends once again into the earth. It is the same principle that causes water in the bottom of a pot on a stove to rise, to be replaced by cooler water from the surface.

In the case of the earth, the continents, which float on the mantle, are carried along with this stream in much the same way as scum or foam is carried along the surface of a liquid. But unlike the water in a pot, the process is incredibly slow. It has been at least 150 million years since the Americas were connected to Europe and Africa. And since Columbus discovered the New World, it has drifted only 30 feet farther from the Old World.

Continental drift, combined with volcanic activity, will eventually give the earth an appearance quite different from that of today. The volcanic "ring of fire" that surrounds the Pacific Ocean will build more and more island chains. The forces of uplift may eventually rebuild the land bridge that once linked Siberia and Alaska. It was such a land bridge that the Eskimos and American Indians crossed tens of thousands of years ago to populate North America. The southern tip of South America may reach out to join Antarctica, while the narrow neck of land known as the Isthmus of Panama may sink into the sea, separating North and South America. But the Caribbean Sea may become almost completely enclosed as the islands of the West Indies continue to rise, and the two Americas could be connected by a new isthmus. The continents, which have been growing for thousands of millions of years, will continue to grow.

The Ice Age, which covered much of the earth's surface with glaciers as recently as 15,000 years ago, is also under continuing investigation. The most extraordinary piece of detective work has been done by Nobel Prize chemist Harold Urey and his associates Caesare Eminini and Sam Epstein. By measuring the amount of two isotopes of oxygen in fossil sea shells, the Urey group found they could determine the exact temperature of the sea water in which ancient sea creatures lived. So delicate is the measurement that merely developing the instrument that could make it took the Urey group four years. The technique they developed is so exact that it can even pin down the season of the year in which an ancient oyster was born and the number of years it lived. Using this method on fossils of the last 300,000 years. Urey's colleagues found that ocean temperatures throughout the recent ice-ages have varied by about 5°C. in a 40,000-year cycle, which corresponds exactly to the advance and retreat of the glaciers on land.

This temperature cycle supports an old theory of the ice-ages proposed by the Serbian physicist Milutin Milankovitch in the 1920's. He found that every 40,000 years circumstances should combine to give the higher latitudes of earth cool summers and mild winters—summers in which glaciers would not melt very much, and winters in which the snowfall would be heavy over the arctic regions and high mountains where glaciers form.

This theory is based on the fact that the earth's tilt in relation to the sun is not constant. The earth's axis now leans at an angle of 23½ degrees, and as we have mentioned, it is this tilt that causes our seasons. If the tilt were increased, the result would be colder winters and warmer summers; if the tilt were decreased, winters would be milder and summers cooler.

It is this second situation that favours the birth of huge ice-age glaciers. Despite the fact that winters would not be as cold, there would still be snow in the far northern and southern latitudes. Cooler summers would mean that less of this snow would melt each year. Thus there would be a build-up of snow, and as new snow was added, the bottom layers would gradually be compressed into ice.

This is the way glaciers form today. But today's glaciers are confined to the far north and south and to a few high mountain peaks in warmer climates (for example, in Glacier National Park in Montana). In an ice-age, glaciers can form much farther from the Poles than they do at present. Growing from year to year, they can eventually cover much of the earth's land surface. In the last ice-age, glaciers reached as far south as St. Louis, Missouri, and in some areas reached a thickness of a mile or more.

The Milankovitch theory explains why temperatures have fluctuated during the ice-ages, but it does not explain why the ice-ages first began. During most of geologic time the temperate regions have enjoyed balmy, subtropical climates; fossils of palm trees have been found only a thousand miles from the North Pole. Within the last 30 million years, according to the Urey group, the bottom waters of the ocean began steadily getting colder, falling from 21°C. at the end of the era of dinosaurs to a mere 20°C. at the beginning of the ice-ages a million years ago.

The theory of continental drift may explain why the earth seems to be becoming cooler. Perhaps in the far distant past the continents were arranged so that the North and South Poles were in the middle of large bodies of water. As long as the Poles were at sea, their ice packs must have been held in check by the warmth of the

The Death of the Sun

SHINING NORMALLY, the sun is seen above the earth at the strength it has had for 5,000 million years and will have for 5,000 million more. After that, scientists believe, it will heat up and burn out.

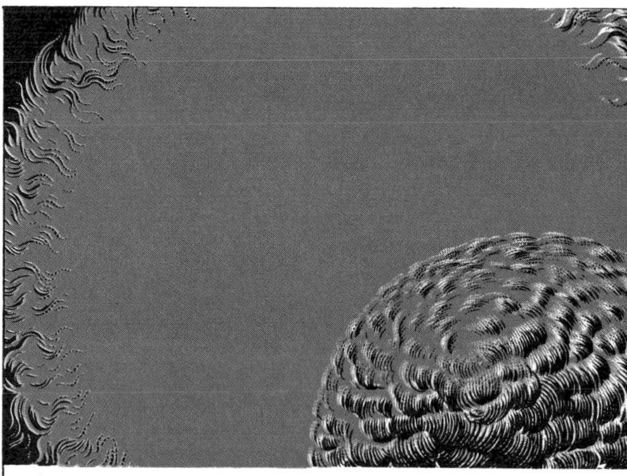

HELIUM forming at the sun's core will gradually expand. It will transform the sun into a type of star called a "red giant", giving off so much heat that the earth's oceans will turn to steam.

ocean. But when Antarctica, Canada, Siberia and Greenland turned frosty white, and thus reflected more sunlight, the earth must have taken in less of the sun's heat every year. Gradually the whole earth, including the oceans, must have grown colder. When the oceans were no longer able to supply enough heat to counteract the trends on land, the glaciers were free to advance and retreat in response to the Milankovitch cycle. In all likelihood the glaciers will come again, many times, to plague man and all living things. However, the latest estimate is that they will not return for 80,000 years.

The best evidence indicates that the climate reached its warmest about 4000 B.C. and has been cooling down since then. But the cooling process has not been a steady one. Its fluctuations seem to have coincided with several great historical events. The warm era some 6,000 years ago probably dried up the Sahara and forced the people of North Africa into the oases of the Nile, where they founded civilizations. Prolonged cold spells may have forced the barbarian hordes south-westwards out of Central Asia to invade the lands of the Roman Empire. A balmy spell around A.D. 1000 probably enabled the Vikings to discover Iceland, Greenland and America. Since about 1720 the ocean temperature has risen slightly, but there is no reason to believe that it will not soon go down again.

If glaciers do grind slowly south again over the next tens of thousands of years, man will either have to migrate into the tropics and desert zones of the earth, or he

SHRINKING AGAIN, after about a thousand million years as a red giant, the sun will return to its present size above a scorched earth. But it will be dying, and its brightness will have begun to fade.

NEAR DEATH, the sun will be a "white dwarf", about 15,000 million years from now. Its fires almost extinguished, it will give off so little heat that the earth will become a dark and frozen mass.

will have to spend considerable power and ingenuity, altering the climate in such a way that the advance is halted. If, on the other hand, the earth heats up again, the ice-ages will come to an end. The tremendous volume of water locked in the ice caps of Greenland and Antarctica will melt, raising the level of the oceans perhaps 100 feet or more over a long period of time. In this event too man will either have to move or expend enormous energy and intellect. Either he will have to abandon his present coastlands and great port cities or rebuild them, using land fill and dikes extending for many miles.

Modern man, by his very existence, may help to bring these rising seas about. Over the last 100 years, factory chimneys have poured a thousand million tons of carbon dioxide into the atmosphere, increasing its carbon dioxide content by about 10 per cent. Since carbon dioxide in the atmosphere prevents the escape of heat from the earth into space, this change in the air's content may have raised earth temperatures by about one-twentieth of a degree in the last century. Although this is a very small difference, it may grow larger. In A.D. 2000 a possible million, million tons of CO_2 will increase the earth's average temperature still further.

But the labours the earth may require of the human race during future floods and glaciations will be nothing compared to the challenges from outside the earth. The first threat will come from the moon. The tides it raises in the land, sea and air are gradually slowing down the earth's spin. At

(Text continued on page 122)

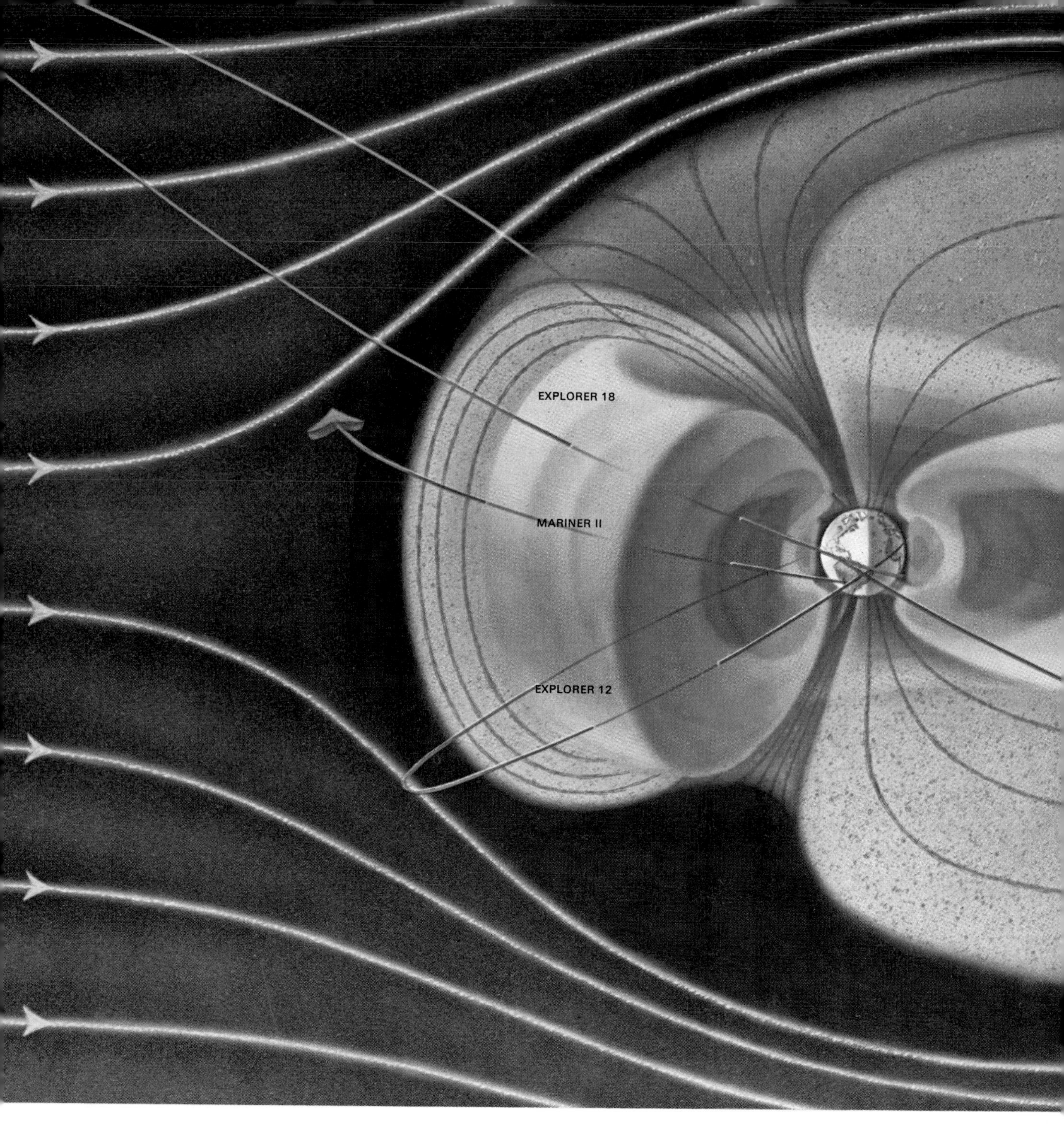

A Cloak of Radiation

Surrounding the earth are several vast layers of radiation particles trapped in the earth's magnetic field. These layers were detected by the first American satellite, Explorer I, and others since then have yielded more information. (The satellites' paths are shown in red.) The layers are called the Van

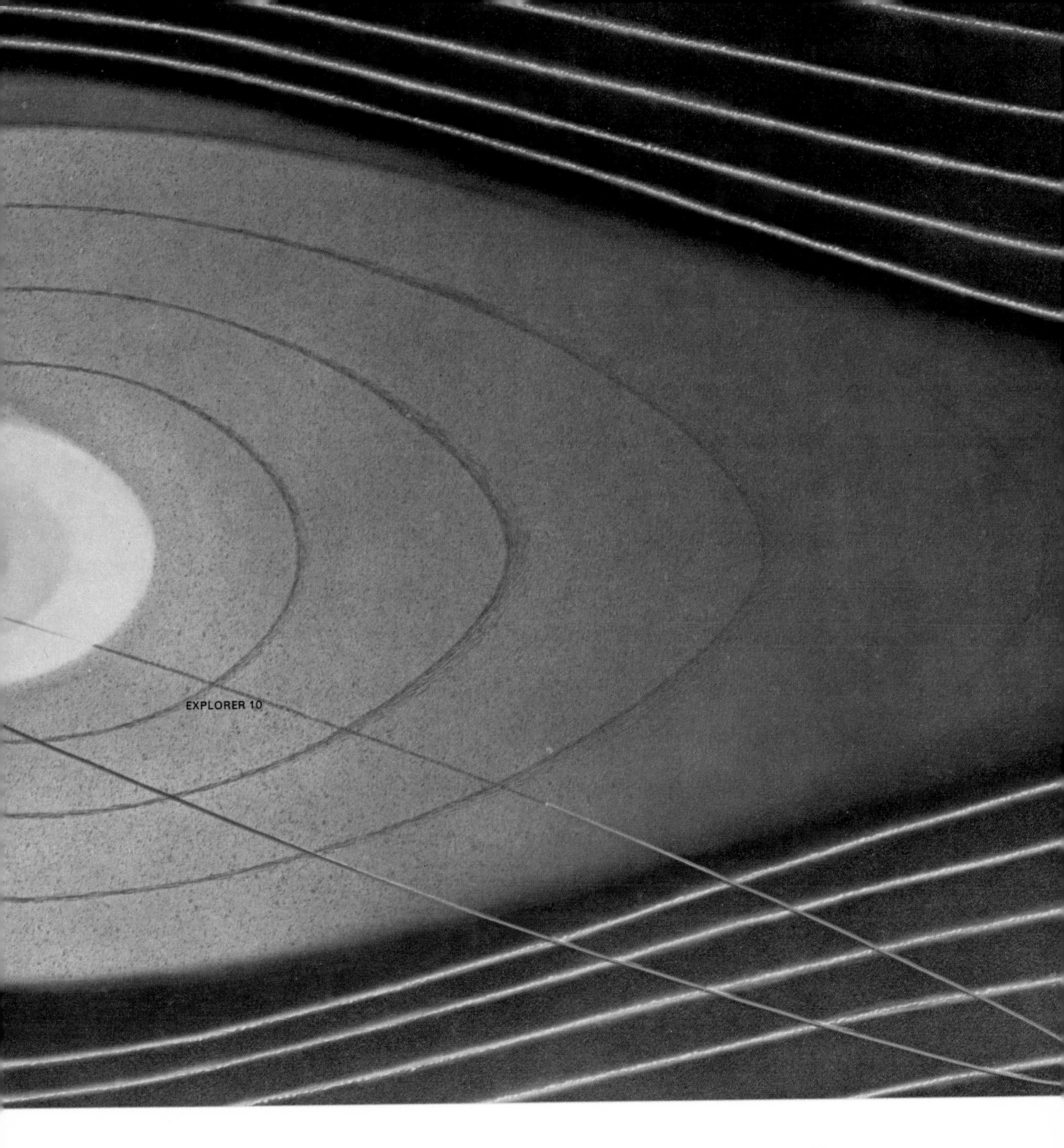

Allen belts, after Dr. James van Allen, who identified them. They extend 50,000 miles towards the sun (*left*) and, buffeted by the solar wind, a stream of radioactive particles constantly given off by the sun (yellow lines), they trail off on the other side of the earth. There are two main kinds of particles in the belt: negative particles, or electrons (shown in blue), and positive particles, or protons (pink and orange). Without these belts, life on earth, as we know it, would probably not be able to exist. The belts shield the earth from much of the lethal radioactivity given off by the sun.

present the rotation period is lengthening at the rate of about 25 thousand-millionths of a second each day. This seems very small, but after 5,000 million years it will give the earth roughly a 36-hour day. Man and his crops should be able to adjust themselves to the warmer 18-hour days and to the equally long, colder nights.

The earth's slowing rotation will be accompanied by a second phenomenon: the moon will begin to move into a larger orbit. It will spiral outwards from the earth and shine more faintly in the sky. At present the moon is departing from the earth by about one foot every 30 years.

The gravitational pull of the sun also affects the earth. The sun has always been working with the moon to slow the earth's rotation, and it will continue to do so. At one time, about 375 million years ago, the earth had a 400-day year. This was not because it took the planet any longer to travel around the sun than it does now, but because the days were shorter—slightly less than 22 hours long. Some time in the future—perhaps in 5,000 million years or so—the sun and moon will have slowed our planet's spin so that a day is 720 hours long—as long as a month. The moon now rotates once on its axis as it makes one complete revolution around the earth, and thus always keeps the same face towards us. When the earth's rotation is sufficiently slowed, it will always present the same face to the moon. When this happens the moon will be nearly half again as far from the earth as it is today.

Astronomers know exactly how the sun will evolve because they have studied sun-like stars that are older than our sun, and have seen how they behave as they begin to run out of the nuclear fuel that makes them burn. When a star of the sun's mass has converted 15 per cent of its original hydrogen into helium, the helium ash that has formed at its core lights up in a second nuclear reaction that is far hotter. As a result the star begins to pour out energy at an increasing rate, swelling and turning blood red in the process.

About 5,000 or 6,000 million years from now the sun will bloat up from its present size until it almost touches its innermost planet, Mercury. At the height of its power, the sun's outpouring of energy will raise the temperature of the earth to between 500 and 600°C.—a heat so intense that the oceans will turn to steam, and sulphur will boil on the earth's surface.

After the deadly climax of its life, the sun will gradually shrink again and this steaming atmosphere will condense once more, flooding the earth. For a few hundred million years the sun will burn blue as it converts the last of its nuclear fuels into metallic elements. During the course of its old age it may undergo eruptions in its outer layers, eruptions that will lay bare its blazing interior and expose the earth to devastating doses of X- and gamma-rays.

Finally, the sun will use up the last of its nuclear energy. The waters of the earth will then freeze into a permanent mantle of ice. As the sun cools further, it will continue to shrink under its own weight and will glow feebly for a long, long time. At last, after a lifetime of some 60,000 million years, the sun, now completely dark, will course onwards through space only as the black corpse of a star, shrunken to incredible density and taking up no more room than a planet. In its final state it will actually be smaller than the earth, but its dense mass will still keep the earth locked in orbit around it.

While the sun is dying, the days on earth will have grown even longer than a month, and the behaviour of the moon will begin to change. It will cease its outward spiral and start its long journey back towards the earth; each orbit will be slightly smaller than the last. The moon will reach its present orbit, some 240,000 miles from earth, and continue to get nearer. But in all likelihood it will not collide with the earth. If it comes close enough—within 9,000 miles—it will probably shatter, torn apart by the force of the earth's strong gravitational pull. The moon fragments will eventually distribute themselves evenly in a belt that will circle above the earth's equator. If there are still humans on the planet in that far-off time, they will see not one moon, but tens of thousands of tiny moonlets. From outer space, the earth will closely resemble that other ringed planet of our solar system, Saturn.

But today's theorists are beginning to doubt that the sun will remain hot enough long enough for this to happen. They suggest that the sun may go through its final phases too quickly for the earth to have a chance to bring the moon within shattering distance. Instead, the moon's tidal effects may take over again and the moon may once more pull away from the earth. As it drifts off it will have little light to reflect from a dim and dying sun, and the nights will become darker and darker until the moon is no longer visible at all.

Scientists assume that the human race will not live long enough to suffer in the fiery swelling of the sun or the dark doom of the moon. The average life of any one animal species is only about one million years—one million years compared to 5,000 million years before the sun even begins to swell. Even though man will probably fare no better than other animals, there is just a chance that he might. Some species have survived unchanged on earth for hundreds of millions of years. What is more, the human species is not subject to the same laws of evolution that have operated up to now. Already man so dominates his planet that the natural evolution of most land plants and large animals has been drastically altered. Man's own evolution has also escaped from the natural channels.

Most scientists take a gloomy view of man's ability to survive his own warlike nature. Yet if the human race does outlive its murderous instincts, it may well plan to outlive the sun as well. Colonizing other planets around stars burning more slowly than the sun may possibly provide a temporary escape for a few fortunate astronauts. The rest of the earth's inhabitants, however, would have to devise a different kind of escape.

At its worst, the sun might not scald the earth with heat and cosmic rays so deadly that men could not invent shields against them. It may be that when the heat-death approaches on earth some 5,000 million years from now, men will already have gone underground, taking with them as much of the earth's air and water as possible and coating the outside of their shelters with mirrors to reflect the sun's scorching heat. As the sun cools, man may be able to come out of his artificial caves into the open again and devise a new kind of life.

Of course this is all speculation. No one can see as far as this into the future. But science has found no reason for man's not being able to extend his evolution almost indefinitely—if only he can learn to use his intelligence for his own best ends.

Is Anyone Talking out There?

Shown in a star-streaked time exposure, the antenna of a big radio-telescope "listens" for radio signals from space. Such telescopes have detected mysterious radio signals, called "pulsars", from several different parts of our galaxy. One day they may locate signals from other intelligent forms of life.

INDEX

Numerals in italics indicate a photograph or painting of the subject listed.

Credits

The sources for the illustrations that appear in this book are shown below. Credits for the pictures from left to right are separated by commas, from top to bottom by dashes.

Cover—Juan Guzman
Table of Contents—Joseph Bertelli—Adolph E. Brotman—Dan Todd—Matt Greene—Lowell Hess—Adolph E. Brotman—Axel Ebel
6—NASA
8, 9—Joseph Bertelli
10-11—Antonio Petruccelli
12—Matt Greene
14-15—Joseph M. Secacca courtesy American Museum of Natural History—Ralph Crane from Black Star, Hugh Morton from Alpha Photo Associates, Inc.
16-17—Mel Hunter
18-19—Lick Observatory Photo, NASA—NASA
20-21—Jack Birns—J. R. Eyerman
23—Frank J. Scherschel
24-25—Gordon Parks
26, 27—Eliot Elisofon, Camera Hawaii from Alpha Photo Associates, Inc.
29—David Klein
30—Brian Brake from Magnum
32-33—Courtesy International Seismological Survey
34, 35—Adolph E. Brotman
37—Carnegie Institute of Washington—Carl Mydans
38, 39—Fritz Goro, J. R. Eyerman
41—Fairchild Aerial Surveys, Inc.
42-43—Eliot Elisofon
44, 45—Nicholas Fasciano
46-47—Dan Todd
48-49—Eric Schaal, Victor H. Waldrop
50-51—Royal Meteorological Society except centre top Jesse Lunger from Black Star
52-53—Ted Bank from Monkmeyer Press Photos, Horace S. Benson courtesy General Electric Corp., Yitka Kilian, U.S. Naval Ordnance Laboratory
54, 55—Bill Burkett, George Yates for *The Des Moines Register*.
57—Weather Bureau Miami, Florida, courtesy NASA
58-59—Daniel Farber from Rapho Guillumette
61—Richard Jepperson from Alpha Photos
62-63—Grant Heilman
64-65—Emil Schulthess from Black Star, Josef Muench (2), Douglas P. Wilson, Robert Walsh, Emil Schulthess from Black Star
67—Nino Carbe
68, 69—Josef Muench, art by Matt Greene
70, 71—Bradford Washburn, William M. Lee
72, 73—Ray Atkeson
74, 75—Andreas Feininger, Nicholas Fasciano courtesy Dr. Luna B. Leopold
76, 77—N. R. Farbman
78—Walter Dawn
81, 82—David Klein
84—R. H. Chapman U.S. Geological Survey
86, 87—Lee Boltin except drawing Lowell Hess
89—Lee Boltin except drawing Lowell Hess
90—Lee Boltin (3)—Paul Jensen, Lee Boltin (2)—Paul Jensen (2), Lee Boltin—drawing by Lowell Hess
92—Dmitri Kessel, courtesy American Museum of Natural History—Dmitri Kessel (2)—courtesy American Museum of Natural History, Dmitri Kessel
93—Dmitri Kessel, Russ Kinne from Photo Researchers Inc.—courtesy American Museum of Natural History, Dmitri Kessel—Floyd R. Getsinger, courtesy American Museum of Natural History
94, 95—Bob Landry, Lee Boltin, Margaret Bourke-White
97—George Silk
98—National Park Service
100-102—Adolph E. Brotman
104—Adolph E. Brotman
105—Antonio Petruccelli
107—top left Mark A. Binn, top right (2) Carroll Lane and Mildred Adams Fenton—courtesy F. M. Carpenter
109—William Schopf and Elso S. Barghoorn—U.P.I.—William Schopf and Elso S. Barghoorn
111—Carroll Lane and Mildred Adams Fenton
112—Mel Hunter
114, 115—Alex Ebel
118, 119—Alex Ebel
120, 121—Max Gschwind for FORTUNE
124, 125—Andreas Feininger
End papers—Gloria Cernosia

For Further Reading

Adler, Irving and Ruth, *Weather in Your Life*. John Day Co., 1959.
Ames, Gerald, and Rose Wyler, *Planet Earth*. Golden Press, Inc., 1963.
Asimov, Isaac, *The Double Planet* (rev. ed.). Abelard-Schuman, 1967.
Burton, Virginia, *Life Story*. Houghton Mifflin Co., 1962.
Chandler, M. H., *Man's Home: The Earth*. Rand McNally, 1965.
Fenton, Carroll Lane, and Mildred Adams Fenton, *Rocks and Their Stories*. Doubleday, 1951.
Jensen, David E., *My Hobby Is Collecting Rocks and Minerals*. Childrens Press, 1958.
Lauber, Patricia, *Junior Science Book of Volcanoes*. Garrard Publishing, 1965.
Pearl, Richard M., *Wonders of Rocks and Minerals*. Dodd, Mead, 1961.
Pilkington, Roger, *The River*. H. Z. Walck, 1963.
Shannon, Terry, and Charles Payzant, *Project Sealab: The Story of the United States Navy's Man-In-The-Sea Program*. Golden Gate Junior Books, 1966.
Spar, Jerome, in co-operation with the American Museum of Natural History, *The Way of the Weather*. Creative Educational Society, 1962.
Zim, Herbert S., *Rocks and Minerals: A Guide to Familiar Minerals, Gems, Ores and Rocks*, Golden Press, 1957.

Acknowledgements

The editors are indebted to Dr. Wallace S. Broecker, Professor of Geology, Columbia University, New York City, New York, who read and commented on the entire text. The editors are also indebted to the staff of the LIFE Nature Library edition of *The Earth*, from which this volume has been adapted. The staff for this edition was Ogden Tanner, editor; Eric Gluckman, designer; Jonathan Kastner, Marianna Kastner, writers; Eleanor Feltser, Susan Marcus, Theo Pascal, Kelly Tasker, researchers; E. W. C. and V. M. Wilkins, adaptors; Gloria Cernosia, art assistant.

Finito di stampare nel mese di Ottobre 1969 presso le Officine Grafiche Arnoldo Mondadori - Verona - Printed in Italy